NO LONGER A STRAY

NO LONGER A STRAY

The Gospel according to PupPup

TERRY DEFFENBAUGH

Illustrated by Joseph Knisely

Scepter

Published by Scepter Publishers, Inc.
www.scepterpublishers.org

ISBN 1-59417-005-3

THIRD PRINTING, MARCH 2006

Text composed in Monotype Plantin

Printed in the United States of America

Preface

I am not a Scripture scholar, nor a theologian with a doctoral degree. I am an Augustinian priest, a retreat director, a youth minister, and a storyteller. All of these roles I consider gifts from God. My ministry involves trying to make God—the Father, Jesus, the Holy Spirit—and Scripture and our Catholic tradition come alive for those I meet.

I've written *No Longer a Stray* so that the reader might experience what it might have been like to be right there with Jesus. I've used the Gospels as a springboard, and tried to flesh out the people we hear of in Jesus' life. Because certain incidents are found in different sequences in the four Gospels, some of the Gospel stories are presented in a different order than might be expected. I have also expanded on some of the personalities of whom little is known. I didn't try to put everything in this work. You'll find, for instance, that I left out most of the parables. I did this because they are stories already, and can be read in the New Testament. You will likewise find a few personalities in the story that are not in the Gospels. They came out of my imagination. I hope that they were seeds sown by a being higher than me, and that God is pleased with my work.

Why I chose the narrator that I did has a lot to do with animals that I have encountered, who, I sometimes feel, understand more than they're given credit for.

I hope that you will enjoy the story, and that it helps you to build your own relationship with Jesus and to understand your own calling as a Christian. For me, writing this story has been like a spiritual exercise, and I am truly grateful to all the people who challenged me to do it. And most especially to God, who I feel gave me a big push to start it, and even more help to complete it. Thank you, God, for finding me, and for being my Master.

NO LONGER A STRAY

I

"Do You Want to Come with Me?"

Hi! Let me tell you a little about myself. My name—well, that's a bit of a problem. You see, until fairly recently I didn't really have a name. What people called me was Hey You, or Mutt, or Stray.

I can't much remember my parents—they were taken away from me when I was real little. So I had to survive as best I could on the street. I had to find food where I could—garbage, handouts when I was lucky. I even stole from stores, just to stay alive.

This, of course, made me unpopular in the neighborhood. Which, by the way, was in Nazareth.

The people there would chase me away, throw things at me, and call me names. Living on the street as I did, I was dirty and smelly and had matted-up hair. I was seriously not cute. I felt my life was terrible and getting worse.

But that's all changed.

One day I'm in an alley. I have just been chased by a shopkeeper and am hiding. I hear some footsteps, and think, This could be the end for me. I'm so scared, I am trembling.

But it's not the shopkeeper, it's someone else. And the first thing I notice about him is his eyes. They are the gentlest eyes I've ever seen.

This man sees me hiding and asks, "What's wrong?" in a voice both gentle and strong. For the first time in a long while, I'm not afraid of a man.

He carefully picks me up and holds me close to him. And right away I stop shaking.

"Do you want to come with me?" he asks.

9

Oh, *do* I want to go with him. So I wag my tail, and he says, "Okay, then, let's go home."

He carries me all the way to his home. I have never felt so loved in all my life.

This gentle man brings me into a combination house and shop. It looks like a carpenter's shop.

When we come in, a woman turns around. She is very pretty, and has those same gentle eyes that he has. She smiles at him and says, "Jesus, what have you brought home now?"

So that's his name—Jesus.

"Mom," he says, "it's just a little one who needs some loving care. Is there something you can give it to eat?"

He sets me down on the floor. I right away have a good feeling about what's happening to me. I sure hope this works out. I'm not sensing any of the anger or meanness that I've come to expect when I'm around people.

Jesus' mom puts down a dish with some food in it, and also one with water. I'm so hungry, I start eating as fast as I can. She says, "Well, this little one sure must be starved—look how quickly it's cleaning the bowl."

Jesus says to her, "I'd like to keep this little one. Would you mind having it around the house?"

She says, "Now why doesn't it surprise me that you want to help out the little beggar. Sure, why not? It won't be in the way. And it would be nice to have some company around now that my Joseph is gone."

When she says the name Joseph, they both get tears in their eyes. That must have been Jesus' dad.

Jesus looks at me and says, "Well, first thing, we have to get you cleaned up. You need a bath. I am going to get some water in a tub."

Uh-oh, now I'm in for it. In the past, anytime water has been mentioned, it's always been thrown at me. I want to run. But this man has been so kind to me, I decide to take a chance.

After he gets the water in the tub, I am gently picked up and placed in the water. He very slowly and kindly washes me. And all the time he is washing me, he is humming a little song. I don't recognize it, but it really puts me at ease. And then after the bath he dries me off with a soft towel. I've never been treated like this before.

Then he looks me over and says, "You've got some matted hair that I have to take care of." He takes out a little knife and slowly cuts out all of the clumps of hair. Even though I'm scared, I trust him. It feels like he is real interested in something he thinks I can become.

After I'm cleaned up he takes a good long look at me and says, "Well, what are we going to call you? Now that you've been bathed and fixed up, you look almost like a different dog, or like you just got born all over again. So, how about PupPup?"

His mom looks at me and says, "Yes, it does look like a puppy, but it also looks as if it's picked up some wisdom. I think PupPup is a good name."

Jesus asks me, "Do you like this name?"

I wag my tail. PupPup is the first real name I've ever been given. It sounds wonderful to me.

▲▼▲▼▲

I've been with Jesus for nine months now. I spend all my time with him. When he's working in the carpenter's shop, I lie near the door and watch him. In the house I'm always at his feet. Or I jump up and sit on his lap and he pets me.

When I first met some of the other relatives, I found out that his mom's name is Mary. She is so nice, and every time she looks at him you can see in her eyes the love she has for him. But in the last few months there's also been a worried look in her eyes. It's as if she knows that something is going to be taking her Jesus away from her.

One day I hear him tell her that he feels it's time to take up his "ministry," whatever that means. She tells him that she knows it is, and has been expecting this for some time. But when he goes back into the shop, she starts crying. I stand back a bit, confused by what I'm seeing. He loves her so much, why would he do something that makes her cry?

▲▼▲▼▲

Then, a week or so later, he sells the shop! He is moving Mary into a little house, really only big enough for one. He's packing a few things for himself, and getting everything settled for Mary.

I'm getting scared. Am I going to be kicked out on the street again?

I hear them talking about me. Jesus asks Mary if she wants to keep me as protection when he leaves. But she says, "No, you keep Pup. Our little friend will be a good companion for you on your journeys, and I still have family here."

Jesus says, "I'll invite Pup to come along. It will be Pup's decision—to stay at home with you, or go back on the street, with me."

▲▼▲▼▲

Today is the day. Jesus tells his mom that he is leaving on a "mission," something he knows is God's will. She says, "I know it is. Go with God, and know that you are always in my heart." And he says, "I know, and I love you very much. This is just something I have to do." They hug a long time, and they both have tears in their eyes.

He goes to the door, looks at me, and says, "Well, Pup, are you going to stay home with Mom, or are you coming with me?"

I love Mary. I wish I could go *and* stay. I look at her, and she says, "Go on, Pup. I know you need to be with him."

What else can I do? He's my Master. I will follow him anywhere.

As we go down the road, Jesus and me, I don't know where we're going or what we'll be doing. But I sense that we're starting an adventure that will make my past life look like it was nothing. At first I am a little scared, but being with Jesus, my Master, makes my fear melt away. I thank God that Jesus picked me up in that alley and is now the one I call Master.

2

"For Me It Will Be a Commitment"

We've been traveling for a while now, in the direction of the sunrise. Jesus seems to want to keep going, but we're not rushing. He really enjoys the people we're meeting, especially the kids.

When there are kids around, his eyes light up. He always lets them play with me, and I love it. When they ask what my name is, he says, "It's PupPup. We found each other in an alley."

When anyone asks where we're going, he says, "I don't really know; we're just following the path God is leading us along." The kids simply accept what he says, but the adults look at him kind of strange when he tells them God is directing him.

I never would have thought I would want to be living on the road again. But now it's different—I'm not alone. I have found that being with someone you love and trust makes any place home.

My favorite times are at night. Although the kids are great, I really love when Jesus and I are all alone at night. I lie next to him and put my head in his lap, and slowly and lovingly he scratches my head. When he does this, I can tell that he is thinking of Mary and how much he misses her.

Sometimes he prays, saying things like, "Father, help me carry out this work you have asked me to do," and "Provide your powerful grace to those who will accept the call to join me." At these times I feel like God is sitting at the campfire with us. I have not figured out exactly what Jesus is, but I know he is more than just a regular person. Of course, I knew that when he picked me up in the alley.

One day, as we are coming over a hill, he says to me, "Well, Pup, there it is—the Jordan River. I hear that my cousin John is somewhere around here. I think we'll stop in and say hi."

I wonder what John will be like. Will he have those same gentle eyes that Jesus and Mary have?

It takes us some time to find him. When we do, we are up on a hill, looking down at a large group of people.

Jesus sits under a tree and says to me, "Looks like my cousin is busy. Let's stay here and watch him work for a while."

As I sit beside him, I look all around. Jesus notices my confusion, and says, "Oh, you're wondering which one is my cousin." He points and says, "That's him—the one they are calling the Baptizer."

I am shocked at who Jesus is pointing to. John is dressed not at all like Jesus. He is wearing what looks like a long shirt made out of some kind of animal skin. And his eyes are not gentle; they are full of fire. And he speaks in a very fierce way.

He is telling all these people, in no uncertain terms, that they need to give up sin and straighten out their lives and so "prepare the way of the Lord!" And when anyone comes up to him and accepts that challenge, he dunks the person in the Jordan and then shouts, "Thanks be to God!"

I notice that Jesus is enjoying watching and listening to his cousin.

Suddenly the crowd parts, and through the middle of it come some men, rather well dressed. As these men approach John, some of the people in the crowd remark, "Oh, boy, here come the Pharisees and the Sadducees."

John is clearly surprised to see them here, and not pleasantly so. He asks them very gruffly, "What have *you* come for?"

They answer, "We want to be saved by the water you are pouring over the people."

John shouts, "You swarm of snakes! The water will do you no good unless you truly repent of your wicked ways and prove it by doing good! Don't think for one moment that you can fool God!"

As all this is going on, I glance up at Jesus, and sense how proud he is of his cousin. Then he looks at me and says, "You know, Pup, it takes a lot of guts to challenge the high and mighty. He's left no doubt that he knows they were just trying to use him for their own selfish ends. But someday, I'm afraid, this message he is spreading for God will get him in big trouble."

We look down again, and see the Pharisees and Sadducees leaving—and not looking very happy. They shake their fists at John and swear to even the score later. But the other people start cheering John and calling him a great prophet.

He turns to them and says, "Don't cheer me. I'm only preparing the way for someone much greater than me; someone so great that I'm not worthy to do the simplest task for him. I haven't been told yet who it is, but God will let me know when that greatest of all prophets, our Messiah, is in our land. Let's all pray that the time is soon, and prepare for it by giving our lives over to the Lord God, by our good works of sharing what we have and being kind to one another."

He then goes back to dunking people in the Jordan after they promise to change.

Jesus looks at me and says, "I think it's time for me to go see John. Pup, you stay here. Don't worry, I'll be back for you."

I don't like the idea of letting him go to the river alone, and he senses that. He says, "It's something I have to do alone. You, Pup, don't have any need for this baptism. Actually, I don't either, but for me it will be a commitment to something much greater than my cousin can imagine."

As he leaves, he pats me on the head, and I know everything is going to be all right. I lie down to watch what happens.

When Jesus gets halfway down the hill, John catches sight of him, and he stops what he is doing and turns to him. At first I think it's just that he recognizes his cousin. But then the look on his face tells me that he is seeing something more. He points to Jesus and shouts, "This is the one that God destined me to prepare the way for! The one now coming to the river is going to bring to us all a life with no end! He is our Messiah!"

I can't believe what I am hearing. And I'm not sure I want to. Jesus looks a little uneasy when John makes that announcement.

Jesus then says, "Cousin, do for me what you have done for so many others."

John shouts, "No! You should be the one baptizing me! I'm not worthy even to take your shoes off!"

"No, John," Jesus insists, "this is the way God destined it to happen that you fulfill your mission. Please do it, now!"

As John baptizes Jesus, all of the people at the river keep staring.

When Jesus comes out of the river, the sky seems to rip open, and a white dove swoops down and hovers over him. Then, from the clouds, there comes a booming sound, like the voice of some very powerful being. Jesus looks up and stares intently. I could swear that I hear a voice say, "This is my Son. I am proud of him." And I think I must be right, because Jesus is smiling.

As he walks back up the hill to get me, I hear the people talking. Some are saying that what they heard was thunder, while others are saying they were blessed to have heard the voice of God.

Jesus comes up to me and pets me, and says, "Now, Pup, I think I know what I need to do. I'm glad Mom let you come with me. I know the road will be difficult at times, and I'm going to need a companion who will give me unconditional love, which is what God has asked me to give to all the world. But I have to decide how to carry out what I have been asked to do. For that, I think we need some quiet time to reflect on all that's just happened."

There is a change in Jesus; we are now moving with more purpose. His face shines with a new understanding. We still take time to be with people, both grown-ups and kids. Jesus still laughs and enjoys all the life around him. But I can tell that what happened at the Jordan River has had a big effect on him.

It has also had a big effect on me. I could just swear I heard a voice from the clouds say, "This is my Son. I am proud of him." Can it really be? Jesus, my Master, is the *Son of God*?

3

"All of Your Temptations Are Nothing"

After our visit to John, Jesus goes to the market to buy supplies—and he buys a lot.

I think he can read my mind. He says, "Pup, after what's just happened we need to go to a quiet place and sort this all out. And I'm afraid it will take some time."

As we walk, I notice that the land gets drier and more barren. And after a while we're no longer meeting people on the road.

Now we are in the desert, and Jesus finally finds a place for us to stay. There is a little protection from the hot sun, but it is a place without any comforts.

Jesus looks at me and says, "Pup, this is where the Holy Spirit will help me reflect on my Father's plans for me. Through prayer I will in a special way be united with the Father and the Spirit and will be given the strength to carry out those plans."

Each day, Jesus spends most of his time in prayer. I lie behind him and watch. I also think about what has happened in my life—especially about how Jesus took me in—and about how much he means to me. As hot and uncomfortable as it is, I will not leave him, ever!

Every morning and every night, Jesus makes sure I have something to eat and drink. But after a few days I notice that he's not eating anything.

So the next morning, when Jesus gives me some food, I

push the bowl over to him with my nose. But he says, with a smile, "No, no, PupPup. I've decided not to eat anything. This is called fasting; it's something that helps people get closer to God. Also it will keep my mind clear so that I can understand what my Father is asking me to do. But you are little, and I am sure he would not want you to pray in that same way. Just be my companion; that will be your prayer."

I lap up the water and eat the food, but still feel bad about Jesus not having anything.

It's getting hotter and hotter. I'm starting to worry about Jesus. By now it must be close to forty days that we have been out in this blistering and desolate place. This night, when I crawl up on his lap, I can feel that he is getting weaker.

I lick the sweat from his face, and he smiles and says, "Thank you, Pup. I don't think we'll have to wait too much longer to achieve our goal." I wonder what he is talking about.

▲▼▲▼▲

The next morning, at sunrise, Jesus and I are at our places, praying, when all of a sudden I sense something strange happening. I am afraid, but at the same time determined to protect my Master from anything bad.

I see what looks like a fat man standing in front of us. I don't know where he's come from.

Jesus is so engrossed in prayer that he does not seem to notice what is going on. So I start growling.

Jesus looks at me and says, "Pup, this is part of what I have to confront. Back off. I'll be all right."

The man says to Jesus, "Are you hungry?"

Jesus says, "Yes, very."

"Well, then," says the fat man, "if you are the Son of

God, command these stones to turn into bread. The Son of God should not go hungry."

Jesus says sharply, "Human beings do not live on bread alone. Go away, devil!" And instantly the man disappears.

I run over to Jesus, wagging my tail, and jump up on him. Maybe now we can leave. But he looks at me and says, "No, Pup, not yet. There's more to come."

At noon, Jesus is kneeling in prayer, and again I sense something strange happening. This time I jump up and start barking.

Jesus stands up, and I stand right beside him. And this time he doesn't send me away.

Before us is what appears to be a very beautiful woman. And suddenly we seem to be standing on an extremely high ledge, and she seems to be standing on a cloud.

She tauntingly says to Jesus, "If you are really the Son of God, throw yourself down; for Scripture says, 'God will order his angels to take care of you; they will hold you up with their hands, so that not even your feet will be injured by the stones.' "

Jesus fires back, "But Scripture also says, 'Do not put the Lord your God to the test.' I'm telling you again, leave me!" And instantly we are back at our place of prayer.

I go up to Jesus again, wagging my tail. He pours a little water for me and says, "Pup, we're almost done here, but not quite. We have to do things by my Father's timetable, not ours."

By now, sunset is coming; and already I am feeling afraid.

Sure enough, I once again sense something strange happening. I get up and stand next to Jesus, and he says, "Yes, PupPup, I see what is coming."

It looks like a very handsome king. He is walking toward Jesus right out of the sunset.

When he gets close to us, he says, "Jesus, I want you to see something." He waves his arm across the sky, and all of a sudden, in the clouds, we see all the great kingdoms of the world, with all their wealth and power. Then, in a spooky voice, he says, "All this I will give you. It has all been handed over to me, and I can give it to anyone I choose. All you have to do is kneel down and worship me."

Jesus angrily replies, "Scripture says, 'You shall worship and serve only the Lord your God.' You are Satan! And all of your temptations are *nothing* compared to what has been offered, not only to me, but to all God's people. What God offers is truly good news—everlasting life with God. What you offer is nothing but a lie and everlasting death. Evil One, go back to your hell of worthless wealth, meaningless power, and empty promises!"

The Evil One, as he is leaving, turns around and snarls, "I'm not done with you yet, Son of God! There are other ways to make your life miserable!"

As soon as Satan is gone, a cool breeze blows up and a gentle rain begins to fall. It is so refreshing. Jesus and I so much enjoy the shower that we even dance around in it.

Then I look up at Jesus and he says to me, "Yes, Pup, we can go home tomorrow. I am now ready for what God has in store for me."

That night, we are visited again. But this time I feel no fear. I see what appear to be some servants sent here to take care of us. Jesus picks me up and says, "We have no reason to be afraid of these folks. They are messengers that God sent to help us get back to Galilee, and to make our journey out of this desert more pleasant. They're called angels."

As he holds me, he rubs my ear. He doesn't say anything, but I can feel that this stay in the desert has brought him a new sense of peace.

Tonight I fall asleep quickly and sleep very soundly. And why not? Tonight I don't have to keep watch. God's messengers, the angels, are here to guard us.

In the morning we leave this place of prayer and testing. And as we walk back to Galilee, I notice that the rain has brought the desert to life. Flowers are springing up everywhere. It's as if the whole world has been changed. I know that these weeks have changed me.

We come to a crossroads, and Jesus tells me that the sign says "Galilee." This is the road we take.

As I walk with Jesus, I can't stop thinking about what these forty days have been like. They have been both horrible and wonderful. Each day I have learned more about my Master—my Master who hates so much the kinds of power that Satan uses as bait, and who at the same time loves so much the kinds of power that God has given all his creatures.

4

"Put Out into the Deep"

When we get back to Galilee, the first place we go is home, to see Mary.

When we get near the house, I run out in front of Jesus, barking. Mary opens the door, and when she sees me and then Jesus, a smile lights up her face. She bends down and pets me till Jesus arrives. Then they give each other a big hug, tears running down their cheeks.

Jesus says, "We won't be here long. I just wanted to see you and tell you how much I've missed you." And Mary, holding on to him, says, "And you know how much I've missed you!"

We spend the day with her, and it is filled with laughter

and love. Jesus doesn't tell her much of what went on in the desert. I think he doesn't want to worry her.

He says, "Tomorrow is the Sabbath; we'll go to the synagogue." She says, "Yes, that would be good."

The next day, when Jesus and Mary are about to go into the synagogue, Jesus looks at me and says, "You'd better stay out here. I don't think they'd let me bring you in."

I feel hurt, but pretty sure that he's right. And I see another good reason for me to stay out here. Although many of the people are smiling at Mary and Jesus and welcoming them, the words of a few of them seem false. So I find a little opening from which I can keep an eye on what's going on.

They invite Jesus to open the service with a reading, and he agrees to. He stands up, unrolls a scroll, finds what he is looking for, and reads, "The Spirit of the Lord is upon me, because he has anointed me to bring good news to the poor. He has sent me to proclaim liberty to captives and gaining of sight to the blind, to set free the oppressed, to announce a year of favor from the Lord."

Then he puts the scroll down and says, "Today this scripture has been fulfilled, in your hearing."

He sits down, and I hear many people praise him for these beautiful words. But I also hear some grumble, "How can he speak like this? Is he not the son of Joseph the carpenter?"

Jesus gets up and says, "I am sure you will quote to me the saying 'Doctor, heal yourself,' and challenge me to do here in my hometown what I've done in Capernaum. But I tell you, a prophet is never welcomed in his hometown."

This seems to make them angry. I glance over at Mary, and she looks frightened and is starting to cry. I jump up and run into the synagogue to be with Jesus, and just then a bunch of men grab him by the arms and drag him outside. They are talking about throwing him down a steep hill.

In the confusion, with everyone running around, Jesus and I slip away. They look for us, but can't find us. We see Mary in the distance. She's the only one who knows where we are. She smiles, and waves us away so that we won't get hurt.

That night, when Jesus and I are sitting by our camp-fire, he says, while petting me, "Pup, the message I have come to spread is about the joy that comes of opening up to the love of God and carrying out his will. It is not a matter of following all the stifling rules that the Pharisees have added to God's law. This is part of the good news I'll be spreading. So, in a lot of synagogues we are not going to be very welcome. Our place of worship will, to a great extent, be out under the sun and stars, and wherever people will gather to hear God's truth."

▲▼▲▼▲

We've been spreading this good news for a while now. Many ordinary people love what they're hearing, and the crowds are growing. But all those Pharisees, Sadducees, scribes, and others who feel that they are holier than ordinary people are not happy at all. They point out that Jesus is saying nothing about the detailed observance of the rabbinic laws, or about the honor they think they deserve.

Jesus finds his first helpers at a big lake called the Sea of Galilee. He is explaining God's message to a large gathering, and the people keep trying so hard to get close to us that they almost push us into the water.

Two boats have just landed, and the men in them are cleaning their nets. Jesus asks one of them, a somewhat older and rough-looking guy, "What's your name?"

He answers, "Simon."

NO LONGER A STRAY

Jesus asks him to take us in his boat and move it a little bit out from the shore, so that he can teach the people.

Simon replies, "I'm a fisherman; I don't take passengers."

Jesus turns to the other man in Simon's boat and asks his name.

He answers, "I'm Andrew, Simon's brother."

Jesus says to Andrew, "You were with the Baptizer. I saw you at the Jordan."

Then Andrew recognizes him. He says, "Oh, my goodness! You're that one that John spoke about! We heard that voice from the sky . . ."

Jesus says, "Right."

Andrew turns to Simon and says, "It can't hurt us to help him out. In fact, it's bound to do us a lot of good. He is more than he seems."

Simon grumbles, but tells us to get in the boat.

Jesus picks me up, saying, "Let's go, Pup."

I'm not so sure I want to do this. Being out on water feels dangerous to me. I prefer good solid ground.

Simon and Andrew row out a little way, and Jesus continues to teach the people what it means to live the good news.

When he's finished, he asks Simon, "How was fishing?"

Simon snaps back, "Do you see any fish? We worked all night and caught absolutely nothing!"

Jesus tells him, "Put out into the deep and let down your nets for a catch."

Simon laughs and says, "Let down our nets. You know nothing about fishing. Who do you think you are, a prophet? You may have Andrew fooled, but not me. Fine, we'll go out farther, and we'll see how much you know about fishing."

While Simon is rowing out, he is grumbling and making

rather rude, cutting comments about preachers and their fishing abilities. I'm getting angry, and I start showing my teeth. I've decided to bite him. But Jesus looks at me, smiles, pats me on the head, and says quietly, "Relax, Pup. Just watch—the joke is going to be on Simon."

They stop and let down the nets. Simon turns around and says, "See? Nothing."

All of a sudden the nets seem to snag. Simon and Andrew start pulling, and the nets turn out to be full of fish! There are so many that they're too heavy for the boat.

So Simon calls out to James and John, his partners in the other boat, and asks them to come help with the catch. And when they reach the nets, they too can hardly believe their eyes.

All this time, Jesus is smiling and scratching my ear.

As soon as we get back on shore, Simon says to Jesus, "Go away from me. I am a sinner."

Jesus, still smiling, says, "Simon, if you follow me I will make you a catcher of people, for God."

I can see that Simon feels the way I did when Jesus invited me to follow him. He doesn't know what to do. He has a feeling that it might be safer to stay where he is, but he's also excited by the challenge.

Finally he says to Jesus, "All right, I will follow you. But this is really crazy."

Then Andrew says, "Jesus, after what John the Baptizer said, I too would like to follow you."

Jesus nods and says, "Please join us."

Then Jesus turns to James and John and says, "I could also use you two in our mission."

They nod and say, "Thank you! We were hoping you would ask."

They turn to their father, Zebedee, who is still sitting in their boat, and James says, "Dad, I know this sounds

insane, but we've got to follow this man. It's an adventure we can't turn down. I know you can find some good men who will work the boats with you."

Simon says to Zebedee, "Take my boat too. And tell my wife that I've been called away on business."

Then he quietly says to all of us on the shore, "Business? What *am* I getting myself into?"

Then, turning back to Zebedee, he says, "Tell her I'll keep in touch. And you take care of her while I'm gone."

And then off we go—Jesus and me and these four new helpers.

That night, at the fire, Jesus tells the four newcomers about the message he is spreading. They take in everything he says, and keep getting more and more excited.

Finally they get tired and fall asleep and it's just Jesus and me again. My head is on his lap. As he is petting me, he says, "What do you think of our first four helpers, Pup?"

I shake my head. I don't really know about these people.

Jesus smiles and says, "I know they're a bit rough around the edges, but I am sure they'll work out. You'll see, everything will be fine. Now I think we need some sleep, too."

As I go to sleep, I hear Jesus thanking his Father for all that he has done so far, and asking that he help him find more helpers for this mission.

The next day, out on the road, we run into one of Simon and Andrew's neighbors. This man has a gentle way about him; he strikes me as the kind of person that does not judge others but accepts everyone. His name is Philip.

Philip says to Simon, "I hear from your wife that you've been called away on business."

"Well," says Simon, "it's actually something more than just business. It is something that's going to change my whole life."

Then Jesus says to Philip, "Would you be interested in being part of the fulfillment of the covenant God made with our ancestors?"

Philip takes one look at him and says, "Yes! I would love to be part of that."

Jesus tells him to go get what he will need and meet us down the road.

When Philip joins the group, he is not alone. He comes up to Jesus and says, "This is Nathanael, better known as Bartholomew. I've told him about your mission to fulfill everything in the Law and the books of the prophets. But he has some doubts."

Then he says to Bartholomew, "Go on—tell him what you said to me."

Bartholomew gets a very serious look on his face. Clearly he is trying to think of an acceptable way to put what he has to say.

Finally he just blurts out, "I said, 'Can anything good come from Nazareth?'"

Jesus laughs and says, "I can see that you are a true Israelite! You speak your mind and don't hide your thoughts. You question, and are open to learning the truth. I like that in a person. And actually, I already knew that about you."

Bartholomew, looking puzzled, asks, "How do you know me?"

Jesus smiles and says, "Before Philip called you, I saw you sitting under the fig tree."

For a few moments Bartholomew just stands there, looking stunned.

Then he says, "Teacher, you are the Son of God!"

Jesus laughs again and says, "You believe in me just because I told you where you were? Listen, you will experience much greater and more startling things. I tell you in all seriousness, you will with your very own eyes see God's power at work. So, will you forget your hesitation and follow me?"

And Bartholomew says, "Yes, Lord."

Jesus and I lead the way. The other six walk behind us, talking and getting to know one another.

Jesus picks me up and carries me for a while, and as he is carrying me he whispers in my ear, "We're getting to be quite a family here. I bet you never imagined anything like this happening, did you, Pup?"

When we left Mary, I knew this adventure would be fun. But I never could have imagined any of what I've experienced. Especially this last part. I mean, where did all those fish *come* from? And how *did* Jesus know about Bartholomew and the fig tree? And then he is called "Son of God" again, this time by Bartholomew . . .

Well, anyway, to me he is my loving Master.

5

"It Was All Mom's Idea"

Jesus and I are always the first ones up. Every morning is the same. Jesus spends some time praying, and I'm there too, thanking God in my own way for Jesus my Master.

When Jesus finishes praying, he always spends some time with me.

One day, while picking me up, he says, "Pup, this is a special day. We've been invited to a wedding. You'll have to stay in the kitchen, but I'm sure there will be some special treats for you there. Best of all, we get to see Mom."

I can't wait. I haven't seen Mary in what seems like a very long time.

Jesus continues, "And Mom's friends have been good enough to invite not only me and you, but also those who have accepted my challenge and become my disciples. I'll start breakfast; you get everyone up and moving so we won't be late."

By this time Jesus has gotten together twelve main helpers. Sometimes I hear them called "apostles," and sometimes "the Twelve," and sometimes, along with other followers, "disciples."

It's not easy waking them all up. These twelve guys are so different from one another. All they've got in common is their love for Jesus and their commitment to the good news he is bringing them. As I go around to make sure everyone is up, it's easy to see the differences.

I first look for Andrew. He's the one we saw with John the Baptizer, at the Jordan River. He turns out to be already up and helping Jesus.

Two others are also up. James, the one whose father is Zebedee, is getting ready the fire for cooking our breakfast. He is one of the three helpers that the rest look up to. Compared to Simon, he is what you would call a quiet leader. He's not afraid of hard work, or of anything else. But now he burns himself stoking the fire, and he bellows in anger. He does have a quick temper.

The third one who is already up is the James whose father is Alphaeus. Sometimes the others call him James Junior, because he's so much younger than the other James. He is also quiet; you might even say shy. But he is always there to help, even without being asked.

Well, those three are up; I better get the rest moving.

I decide to go first to the one I am still not sure I like, and get him over with.

Simon is snoring. Even *that* he does loudly. The others all look to him as a leader, and he is bold, and he does get things done—but he's also really good at putting his foot in his mouth. I know he is truly committed to Jesus, but there are times I still want to bite him, and I do enjoy hassling him. So, I decide to wake him up by jumping on his stomach. I get a big "oofff" out of him, and then he says loudly, "Yeah, yeah, I'm up! Get away from me!" He is not a morning person.

Thomas is next. He always wants to know why something is or isn't happening. And he sure can be moody. But whatever mood he's in, he always has a pat on the head for me. I pull at his covers, and the first thing he says is, "Why do we have to get up so early?" Jesus hears this and says, "We have a wedding to get to, remember?"

John is my favorite. He's the youngest and also the most loving of the guys. Next to Jesus, he is the one who takes care of me the most and shows me the most affection. He gets teased a lot by the others, but I know I can always go to him. I wake him up by licking his face. He grabs me, musses up my fur, and says, "Good morning, Pup."

Thaddaeus is an easy one. I just give a quick bark, and he gets right up and starts folding up his bedding. He is a simple man who watches and listens and follows directions. You can always depend on him.

The next one scares me a little. He always has a sword within reach and is not afraid to use it. This Simon, who usually gets called "the Zealot," is one tough guy. We never have any trouble when traveling with him in the group. He is very proud that Jesus asked him to join us, and lets everyone know it. As I approach him, he jumps up, grabs the sword, and then says, "Oh, it's you, PupPup." I wonder if he ever sleeps really soundly.

Matthew you can tell by his clothing. He used to be a

rich man—a tax collector. The other guys were not so sure about him when Jesus asked him to follow him, but Jesus just told them that he's an honest man. He's the one who gave up the most in answering Jesus' call, and who answered it the most promptly. A simple nudge with my nose gets him moving.

Next will be Judas. Now, that's a hard one to figure out. He seems to always be making secret plans of his own. He appears to love and admire Jesus, but there's just something about him that gives me the creeps. Well, he is already up, and grumbling about the things the group needs to bring to the wedding.

Bartholomew, the one who was hesitant about accepting Jesus' call, is the same with everything he does. I keep pulling on his sleeve to get him up, but it's not working. Finally the Zealot helps me by kicking him on the foot and yelling at him to get up.

Now there's just one more—Philip. We all love Philip. He's like a grandfather to everyone. When I go over to him, he grabs me, holds me in the air, and says, "Thanks, Pup, for letting me sleep the longest." Then he takes some time to scratch my ear.

I run over to Jesus, panting. He looks at me and says, "Did you get them all up? Good, Pup." Then he gives me a taste of the breakfast.

They all gather around to eat, and Jesus leads them in giving thanks for this new day, the food, and all the blessings they've been given by God.

After they eat, he reminds them that they have to hurry. "I don't want to be late for the wedding," he says.

As we come walking up to the place where the wedding is being held, I see Mary, so I run ahead, and when I get to her, she bends down and I jump into her arms. She says, "Did you miss me, Pup?"

My tail is wagging and I am licking her, I am so glad to see her.

When Jesus comes up, she puts me down and gives him a big hug, saying, "PupPup missed me—how about you, son?" And Jesus says, "More than you can imagine."

Jesus introduces his whole group to Mary and the other wedding guests. Then he takes me to the kitchen and asks if it would be all right for me to stay there. Some of the kitchen staff recognize me and say very kindly, "Sure. Pup won't be in the way."

Everyone has a good time. And the kitchen people make sure I keep getting my share of the goodies.

Hours later, I notice Mary and Jesus talking at the kitchen door.

She tells him, "They've run out of wine."

He says, "Mom, it's not the right time; my hour has not yet come."

She says insistently, "But son, it will be so embarrassing for our friends."

Then she turns to some of the serving people and says to them, "Do whatever he tells you to do, even if it sounds a little strange." And with that she goes back to the reception.

Jesus sees me at the door and says to me, "Pup, sometimes my mother doesn't fully understand what I must do when, but how can I refuse her? I love her so much, and you and I have been on the road so long . . ."

Jesus points to six huge stone jars and says to the servers, "Fill those with water."

They do that, and then say, "Now what?"

Jesus tells them, "Draw some out and give it to the head servant. Don't tell him where it came from."

They do as they are told, although they feel really stupid.

After tasting the "water," the head servant calls over the bridegroom and says, "Most people serve the good wine first, to impress everyone. But you've saved it for last. This wine is the best I've ever tasted. You truly are a gracious host."

The bridegroom, having no idea what he is talking about, just thanks him for the compliment.

Mary, having seen and heard all this, smiles at Jesus and whispers, "Thank you," and Jesus smiles back.

Some of the apostles have also witnessed the whole event, and are amazed. They try this wine that used to be water, and even then they have a hard time believing what has happened.

Now we have left the reception. The apostles are walking behind Jesus and me, and talking about what happened to the water. Those who witnessed the event are relating it to the others. None of them knows what to make of it.

Jesus picks me up and says, "Pup, I really did not want to do anything like that just yet. It was all Mom's idea. But God was using her to get everything moving. Certainly it's gotten my disciples talking. I told them they would see God's power at work!"

As he holds me, all I can think of is how very lucky I am, and anyone is, to be loved by my Master.

6

"I Do Want To!"

After the wedding we start traveling around Galilee. Jesus is telling everyone the good news of God's love, and about how we must respond to it by caring for each other, and especially for those in need.

His disciples are helping in all kinds of ways. They talk to those they meet, and try to help them be open to the message.

As for me, my job was best explained when Jesus said to me, "Pup, you welcome everyone and keep us all child-like."

The way people know that the good news is real is by the love that's so obviously there among Jesus and all his followers.

After one of these teaching sessions, as we're walking to where we'll be spending the night, a man comes up and kneels in front of Jesus. The man has an awfully strong smell, which at first I can't identify. But I go up to him anyway to give him my welcome.

And then I see what the smell is. His body is covered with ugly oozing sores. The smell is his own rotting flesh.

I look up at Jesus, wondering what I should do, and I see his eyes fill with tears over what this man has had to suffer. Then he says, "It's okay, Pup, I'll take care of this."

The man says, "Lord, I know that if you want to, you can heal me."

With no hesitation, Jesus reaches out and touches him, saying, "I do want to! Be healed."

Instantly the stench is gone and his skin is totally clear. I wag my tail and lick his hand. His skin is soft as a baby's. He looks at me and pats me on the head. All he can say is a heartfelt "Thank you!" to Jesus.

Jesus says to him, "Don't tell anyone what has happened here. Just go show yourself to the priest and then offer the sacrifice Moses prescribed."

When the man leaves, the disciples come up to Jesus, and before they can say anything, he says to them, "The power of God heals body, mind, and soul."

We all go off to our places for the night.

All of Jesus' followers are quiet, deep in thought. I am lying next to Jesus, with my head in his lap. He, too, is deep in thought, as he is petting me. Finally he says, "I'm glad I could help that man. But I'm afraid he won't be able to keep his joy to himself."

The next morning, when we set out, it is obvious that Jesus was right. The number of people following us is way bigger than before.

Some stay only a short time, but we're hardly ever alone anymore. And almost always there are some spies around, sent by the Pharisees, Sadducees, and scribes.

Later in the day, when we get to Capernaum, a Roman officer comes up to us. I am scared, so I hide behind Jesus, and look at the apostles. Simon and James are on either side of Jesus, ready to defend him if need be. The Zealot is next to James, and has his hand on his sword. The rest of them, I can tell, are as scared as I am.

The officer ignores all this and, with tears in his eyes, says to Jesus, "Sir, a servant of mine—one who is like a member of my family—is very sick and suffering terribly."

Without thinking twice, Jesus says, "I will come to your house and heal your servant."

But the officer says, "Oh, no, I am not worthy to have so great a person in my humble house. I'm just asking you to exert your authority. I know how authority works, because I am a man who has it. I tell a soldier to do something, and it's done. So I know that if you just command that my servant be healed, it will be done."

Jesus turns to the apostles and the other people around us and says, "I have not found faith like this in Israel!"

Then he turns to the officer and says, "Go home. As you have believed, let it be done for you."

The officer thanks him and hurries off.

After he leaves, I hear some of the spies grumbling that Jesus should not even be associating with a Roman officer, much less showing him any kindness.

Jesus says to me, "Pup, why do people have to judge one another? Don't they know that we all come from God and should be respecting and caring for all God's creatures? *All* of God's creatures, from the greatest to the smallest, are gifts from God."

Then he pats me on the head and says, "Simon has invited us to spend the night at his house."

On the way to Simon's house, we get news that the officer's servant is well again.

When we get to the house, Simon's wife comes out to meet us. She is nice-looking, but I also notice that she looks worried. Simon doesn't notice this. He's too busy introducing her to the other apostles and Jesus and me. He tells her, "This is PupPup, Jesus' dog. Pup goes everywhere with him."

But Jesus has noticed right away that something is wrong. So, he asks her what it is, and she says, "My mom is really sick. She has a high fever which just will not break."

Simon laughs and says, "Oh, she'll be all right. She's too mean to die."

Both Jesus and Simon's wife look taken aback. I growl. Simon turns red; he knows he has just put his foot in his mouth again.

Jesus looks away from him and, turning to Simon's wife, says, "Maybe I can help. Would you show me where she is?"

She takes Jesus by the arm and leads him into a small room. There's only room for her and Simon and Jesus and me. The woman on the bed looks very sick, and when I sniff the bed I can feel the heat of her fever.

39

Jesus takes her by the hand and closes his eyes, and I see her getting well. It's as if Jesus is pulling the sickness right out of her body.

When he opens his eyes, she opens hers. Seeing not just us but also those in the next room, she asks her daughter, "Who are all these people?"

Her daughter answers, "They're guests. They're friends of Simon's."

The old woman says, "Well, then, you and I had better get busy if we're going to show them hospitality. Let's get something for them to eat."

Clearly startled, her daughter says, "But Mom, you're sick!"

The mother replies, "Sick? I haven't felt this good in years!" And the two women go into the kitchen to get things ready.

The whole time that we're eating, all the people there keep discussing this healing and some others. When Jesus is asked how he does these things, he just says that it's by the power of God.

After we're done eating, we have a little get-together. I'm on Jesus' lap, and he says to me, "Simon's wife sure is a good cook, isn't she?"

Yes, she sure is. I don't know what she sees in Simon. I guess it must be whatever Jesus sees in him.

It starts getting noisy outside. When we go out, we see that the news of the healings that Jesus is doing has gotten around. People have brought all their sick and demon-possessed friends.

Jesus puts me down and says, "It looks like I have some work to do here, Pup." He goes into the crowd, touching and healing everyone who needs it.

There is this one man who is possessed by a demon that is forcing him to curse and to act very strangely. Jesus looks at the man and says in a powerful voice, "Demon, leave him and let him be healed!"

It looks like a shadow comes out of the man. And from that shadow is heard, "You are the Son of God!"

Jesus, in the same powerful voice, says, "Be quiet!" And nothing else is heard.

That night, when all of the apostles are asleep in Simon's house, Jesus takes me outside into the cool night air. He sits down, and I crawl onto his lap.

"Pup," he says, "there is so much pain in this world. If people only knew that all they have to do is believe in God and let him into their lives, they would be so much happier. And whatever pain they did have would help them grow in holiness. We'll have to keep spreading that message."

As I sit on his lap, I think about the demon that called Jesus "Son of God." Even the evil ones of the world recognize the greatness of my Master.

7

"Be Perfect, as Your Heavenly Father Is"

I'm leading us down the road, as usual. We got a late start today because the Sabbath morning prayer is long. We're heading for the Temple. Jesus shouts to me, "Pup, don't go so fast! We can't all keep up with you, you know, especially since we're tired and hungry!" So I come back and walk next to Jesus.

With us are Jesus' twelve main helpers, and some others who have come to learn more about the good news. Oh, and also some Pharisees, to keep an eye on what we're doing.

As we walk, some of the disciples pluck some ears of

wheat that are growing close to the road. They take one, rub it in their hands, and start munching on the grains. One of the Pharisees shouts out to Jesus, "Teacher, look what they're doing! It's against the Law to do this on the Sabbath!"

Jesus answers, "Haven't you read what David did that time when he needed something to eat? He went into the Temple and ate the bread offered to God. This was when Abiathar was high priest. By our law only the priests may eat this bread, but David ate it, and so did his men."

The Pharisees look not at all happy with what Jesus has said. I jump up on his leg, and he picks me up. Then he continues, "And have you not read in the law of Moses that every Sabbath the priests in the Temple actually break the Sabbath law, and yet are not committing any sin?"

The Pharisees' faces redden with anger.

Then Jesus, rubbing my ear, says, "The Sabbath was made for the sake of people, and not the other way around! Know that the Son of Man is the Lord of the Sabbath."

After this the Pharisees fall silent, and Jesus puts me down.

I notice that some of the Pharisees are going on ahead, so I bark, to warn Jesus of this. He says, "I see them, Pup—they're going ahead to lay the next trap for me."

When we reach the Temple, Jesus picks me up, saying, "I think the only way they'll let you in is if I carry you." And as he walks in, carrying me, they look at him with disgust, but don't say anything.

As we go in, I notice a man with a shriveled and paralyzed hand.

Jesus sits down, and one of the Pharisees stands up and asks, "Teacher, is it against our law to heal on the Sabbath?"

Jesus says, "Do you really want to know, or are you just trying to trip me up?" And then, not waiting for an answer, he says to them all, "What if you had a sheep that fell into a deep hole on the Sabbath? Wouldn't you take hold of it and lift it out?"

Everyone in the Temple nods.

Then Jesus says, "A person is worth much more than a sheep! So, yes, our law does allow us to help a person on the Sabbath."

Most of the people in the Temple seem to approve of Jesus' answer.

Jesus then looks at the man with the useless hand and says to him, "Stand up and stretch out your hand."

The man does as he is asked, and immediately his hand is made well.

The Pharisees start grumbling.

Jesus turns to his disciples and says, "I think we're no longer welcome here. It's time for us to leave."

Many people get up and follow us out of the Temple. The only ones who don't are the Pharisees, the scribes, and the elders. They look angry and seem to be plotting.

Jesus puts me down, and then says, "Pup, look how many people are following us. I feel sorry for those who have stubbornly closed their minds to the truth."

Many of these people from the Temple follow us for days, eager to hear what the good news will mean in their lives.

One day Jesus stops on a hillside and has his helpers get everyone to sit down. Then he sits too, and I lie down by his side.

When he has everyone's attention, he says, "The good news that I am proclaiming is not just words, but a way of life."

James asks, "But what exactly does that mean?"

Jesus looks at the people and says, "Here are some things it means. Blessed are you who are poor in spirit; the kingdom of God is yours! Blessed are you who hunger for righteousness; you will have your fill! Blessed are you who are now crying; you will laugh! Blessed are you when people reject you, and insult you, and falsely say all kinds of bad things about you, all because you are my followers. Be glad when that happens—rejoice!—because a great reward awaits you in heaven. For those very same things were done to the prophets."

"But Jesus," says Simon, "how can this be? You're asking us to live like fools! People will take advantage of us."

"More than you know," says Jesus. "You've heard that it was said to your ancestors, 'Love your friends and hate your enemies.' Well, this is what I say to you: Love your enemies and pray for those who persecute you, so that you can be true children of your Father in heaven. For he makes the sun shine, and the rain fall, on the good and bad alike. Why should he reward you if you only love the people who love you? Even sinners do that much! And if you speak only to your friends, have you done anything out of the ordinary? Don't even pagans do that? You must be *perfect*, as your heavenly Father is."

I look at those sitting around, and see confusion on their faces.

As the crowd starts breaking up, Jesus picks me up and says, "I don't think they all truly wanted to know what the good news means. But everyone here has heard it. It's time for us to go spread it to other towns."

The apostles and a few others stay with us, but the rest of the people go back to their homes. Some of them, I'm sure, will accept Jesus' challenge, but others won't.

A few hours later, as we are coming into the village of Naim, we see a funeral procession coming our way. A woman is crying her heart out. Jesus asks somebody, "What happened?" and they say, "It's very sad. The deceased was the only son of this woman, and she is a widow. We don't know how she'll survive this new loss."

I look at Jesus and see real concern on his face. He looks down at me and says, "Pup, I don't want her to have to suffer this much." Then he turns to his disciples and says, "This is the kind of thing I was talking about when we were up on the hill."

Jesus stops the procession. He goes over to the woman and says, "Don't cry." And then he walks over to the dead man, touches him, and says, "Young man, get up!"

The young man right away sits up and asks what has happened. Jesus turns to the woman and says, "You have your son back. Know that both of you are precious to God."

Now the people start shouting, "A great prophet has appeared among us!" and "God has come to save his people!" But Jesus tells us we need to keep moving if we're going to find a good place to spend the night.

That night, as Jesus and I go off to pray, I hear some of the apostles talking about what Jesus said the good news means, and others discussing what happened in Naim. After spending some time alone in prayer, Jesus invites me up on his lap and says, "Pup, we're giving our helpers a lot to think about, aren't we? But this is just the beginning. The longer they stay with me, the more they'll see the power of God and how it will change their lives." And then he starts rubbing my belly.

I think to myself, Yes, that is true. Since I have been with my Master, I have seen so much, and I have no doubt that Jesus is from God. My life is changed, and will never be the same.

8

"You Did It for Me"

After that last incident in the Temple, the number of spies has grown. Sometimes we have to deal with them practically all day long. Here's an example.

One day we are all gathered at the entrance of the Temple, and Jesus is teaching about the good news, and up comes a member of Herod's party, surrounded by Pharisees. I growl at him, and Jesus says to me, "I know who he is. Watch how he stumbles into his own trap."

The man says, "Teacher, I know that you are a truthful man. You don't care what people think of you; you only care what they think of the truths you teach. Right?"

"Right," says Jesus.

"Well, then," the man continues, "is it wrong to pay taxes to the emperor?"

Jesus says, "You hypocrite. You're just out to trap me, aren't you? Well, show me the coin used to pay the tax."

Someone hands him a coin.

He holds it up and asks, "Whose face is this?"

The man answers, "The emperor's."

"Well, then," Jesus says, "give back to the emperor what belongs to the emperor, and to God what belongs to God."

And then he tosses the coin back to the person who handed it to him.

The questioner and those with him shrink back into the crowd. Jesus looks at me and says, "That was only the first test, Pup. This is going to be one busy day."

Some Sadducees come forward. These people don't believe in an afterlife. I look at Jesus, and he says to me, "Yes, Pup, here comes the next test."

Their leader says, "Teacher, you tell us that there is a life after death."

Jesus nods.

"Well," the man continues, "let me ask you this. Moses, as you know, prescribed for us that if a man's brother dies leaving a wife but no child, the man must marry the widow to raise up children for his brother. All right, suppose there were seven brothers, and this situation kept recurring; one by one, they married this woman and then died, having had no children. In the afterlife, which of them would be her husband?"

Jesus smiles and says, "You think you know the scriptures, but you're looking at heaven from an earthbound perspective. In heaven everyone will be like the angels; there won't be any marriage there.

"God's power goes far beyond the limits of the human imagination. Didn't Moses hear at the burning bush, 'I am the God of Abraham, Isaac, and Jacob'? God is God of the living, not of the dead."

They too shrink back into the crowd, defeated.

I look up at Jesus and think, "This is getting to be fun. Well, at least for us. I don't think our enemies are having too much fun."

Then a teacher of the Law comes up to Jesus.

I'm a little confused by him. He is part of the group trying to trick Jesus, and yet I sense that he really wants to know the truth and live by it. I look at Jesus, and he says to me, "You're right, Pup, this one is different."

The teacher asks, "What is the greatest commandment?"

"That's easy," says Jesus. "It is, Love God with all your heart, soul, mind, and strength. That is the first and greatest commandment. And the second greatest is like it; it is, Love your neighbor as you love yourself. No other rule comes ahead of these two."

The teacher rubs his beard, thinking. Then a look of understanding comes over him and he says, "Yes, God is above all else. Surrendering your whole self to him, loving him with everything you've got, is the only way. And to love others, who also are created by God, as you love yourself—yes, that is true praise of God. And love of God and neighbor is more important than making offerings of burnt sacrifices."

Jesus looks at him with love and admiration and says, "You are not far from truly understanding the good news."

This teacher does not go back into the crowd; he stays and listens to Jesus' words. So I go up to him and jump on his leg. He looks down and pets me, and Jesus says to him, "That's PupPup, a friend who has been with me a long time. Pup is a good judge of people, and knows that you are seeking the truth, unlike others who have questioned me today."

Then Jesus stands up and says to the people, "Do listen to the scribes and the Pharisees. They occupy the chair of Moses, so you should do as they tell you. But do not live like them. They do not practice what they preach. They love to wear fine clothing, and be given the best seats, and be served the best foods. They look good on the outside, but they are like whitewashed tombs—inside is nothing but decay. They do things only for show. They are blind guides, who only think they see the truth. They are hypocrites and descendants of those who killed the great prophets. They will finish the deed started by their ancestors. But this generation's punishment will be the worst of all."

Just then, Jesus catches sight of a poor elderly woman coming up to the offering box. He pauses, to watch her. She puts in two little coins.

Jesus says, "See that woman? All day, those who are well off have been putting in money, but only what they would not miss. Even though they have all put in much greater amounts, this woman has given more than all of them put together, because what she has given is a real sacrifice for her."

Jesus asks a couple of the apostles to bring her over to him. When they do, she looks frightened. Jesus gently says to her, "Don't be afraid. What you have done is truly pleasing to God. You will be greatly rewarded for your gift. In God's name I want to thank you."

When the Pharisees, scribes, and elders hear this, they resentfully call out, "Who are you to make that judgment?"

Jesus says, "Listen, when the Son of Man comes in his glory, and all the angels with him, he will be seated upon a glorious throne, and all the nations will be assembled before him. And he will divide people as a shepherd separates the sheep from the goats, placing the sheep on his right and the goats on his left.

"And then to those on his right the King will say, 'Come, you blessed ones of my Father, receive your reward. For I was hungry, and you fed me; thirsty, and you gave me drink. I was a stranger, and you received me in your home; naked, and you clothed me; sick, and you took care of me; in prison, and you visited me.' The righteous will then ask, 'When did we see you in need and come to your aid?' And the King will answer, 'When you did it for one of the least of these brothers and sisters of mine, you did it for me.'"

Then Jesus points to the old woman and says, "This woman, because she gives what little she has, is counted among the righteous and will be received into the kingdom of God."

Then he continues, "The King will say to those on his left, 'Get away from me, you cursed ones! Away to the eternal fire prepared for the devil and his angels! For I was hungry, and you gave me no food; thirsty, and you gave me no drink; a stranger, and you did not welcome me; naked, and you did not clothe me; sick, and you did not care for me; in prison, and you did not visit me.' They will say, 'Lord, when did we see you in need and not come to your aid?' And he will answer, 'When you did not do it for one of these least ones, you did not do it for me.'"

The Pharisees, scribes, and elders leave, looking, as usual, very displeased.

Jesus and I still have with us the apostles, the old woman, the teacher who wanted to know what is the greatest commandment, and some others who have accepted Jesus' challenge to live according to his teachings. Jesus gathers them all together and thanks and blesses each one. He also tells them, "Be strong when you hear bad things about me. Have faith, because in the end I will win out."

When the only ones left are Jesus and his little band, he says to us, "We need to get some rest, so that we will be ready to celebrate Passover."

As we go back to our place of rest, Jesus tells us, "Some very trying times are coming. Use tonight to reflect on your call and on all that you've learned in your time with me."

Jesus sits, leaning against a tree, and I climb up on his lap. He looks at me and says, "Well, Pup, you've been with me the longest. Are you glad I found you in the alley? And are you glad you chose to follow me and not stay home with Mary?"

I climb up and lick his face. I hope he knows that not only am I glad, I feel *blessed* to call him Master.

9

"He Can Be Happy and Have No Doubts"

One day we notice an unfamiliar group standing at the back of the crowd. At the end of the day they come up to us, and Andrew recognizes them as followers of John the Baptizer.

They ask him, "Will you let us see the Teacher?"

Andrew says, "With pleasure," and introduces them to Jesus.

I run up and sniff them, and judge them to be friends. But I also sense some uneasiness about them. Jesus looks at me as if to ask, "What do you say, Pup?" I wag my tail and sit down.

Andrew tells Jesus, "These are friends of mine, from the time I spent with John the Baptizer at the Jordan River."

Jesus greets them and asks, "And how is my cousin?"

They answer, "He is in prison."

Jesus asks why, and they tell him, "John told Herod that it wasn't right for him to marry his brother's wife. So Herod had him thrown in prison. But that's not why we're here."

"Then why are you?" asks Jesus.

They say, "John asked us to come ask you, are you the one he was to prepare the way for, or are we to expect someone else?"

Jesus replies, "Go back and tell my cousin what you see and hear: the blind receiving sight and the crippled walking; lepers cleansed and the deaf hearing; the dead brought back to life, and the poor having good news preached to them. Tell him he can be happy and have no doubts."

They leave immediately, promising to return with a reply.

After they leave, Jesus says to the crowd, "When you were following John, what did you see? Someone dressed like royalty? No. You found a man fasting and dressed in animal skins. Some of you thought he was a lunatic, or maybe even a demon. He challenged you to repent and be baptized. I tell you, of all those born of women, there has not arisen a greater prophet than John; and yet the lowest person in the kingdom of heaven is greater than he.

"And what do you see in me? I eat and drink with you, and some of you call me a glutton and a drunkard. What you want from me is miracles; what I want from you is that you accept the joy and responsibility of the good news. My cousin John is fulfilling Scripture by preparing the way for me. And he is about to testify to the truth by making the ultimate sacrifice."

People are now getting edgy. Many feel more than challenged; they feel their comfortable way of life being threatened. Many go away, shaking their heads and grumbling, "This Jesus can't speak to us like this. Who does he think he is? Someone greater than John and all the prophets?"

Now it is quiet for us again. I can see that Jesus is tired and a bit sad, and that the apostles are also down. Up till now we've always been mostly welcomed, not rejected, because of his message. I crawl up on his lap and start licking his hand. I want him to know that I love him no matter what. He pets me, and says, "Pup, today I feel I've made some enemies. And I'm also afraid of what will happen to John. I love my cousin, and I wish there was something I could do to help him in this difficult time. But he is the greatest of all prophets, and God will give him the strength to endure all that will be asked of him."

Then Jesus looks around at the apostles and says, "Are you upset with me for shaking up those people? You are with me because I challenged you; you chose to follow me. John's followers responded to his challenges in the same way, and are blessed for it. You need to know that there will be times when we bless the afflicted, but there will also be times when we unsettle those who think they are holy. That way they have an opportunity to repent. And by the way, I have a feeling that our ordeals for the day are not over. A Pharisee has invited us to his house for dinner."

Jesus then looks at me and says, "You come too, Pup. You might not be welcomed, but we'll see how our host will deal with uninvited guests."

The house is a mansion, and looks very inviting. But the Pharisee welcomes Jesus and the apostles with not much politeness, and when he sees me, he actually starts to push me out.

Jesus says to him, with a smile, "Pup is with me."

I can see that the Pharisee doesn't know what to do. For a few seconds he just stands there, and finally he decides to ignore me. I must admit, I am rather enjoying the dilemma of this pompous person. He wants me out, but doesn't want to offend Jesus too openly.

Now he is introducing Jesus to all the big shots of the town. It's obvious that we are being used by this Pharisee. He is showing his friends how important he is, by having the new prophet and healer in his home. I feel very out of place. And I know that Jesus and all the apostles are feeling the same way. I am wondering why Jesus would allow us to be put in this situation.

Just after we start eating, I see a woman come in. I am the first to notice her. When I lived on the street, I used to see women like her. They wear lots of makeup, and only survive by selling their bodies. When I was on the street, these women were the people who were the kindest to me. I guess it was because they too were outcasts.

Jesus is the next one to notice this woman, and when he does, a slight smile appears on his face.

She comes up and kneels in front of him, so I move back and settle under the table. She starts crying, and the tears fall on his feet. Then she wipes his feet with her hair, which is long and beautiful. Then she pours perfume on his feet and starts kissing them.

The host gets up and says, "Jesus, as a prophet you should already know what type of woman this is."

Jesus says, "Let me ask you a question. Suppose one person owed a creditor five hundred pieces of silver, and another one, fifty. Neither could pay, so out of kindness the creditor forgave both of them their debts. Which of them would love the creditor more?"

The host says, "Of course, the one who owed five hundred."

"Right," says Jesus.

The host looks pleased with himself.

But then Jesus continues, "When I arrived, you did not do me even the standard courtesies. You did not have my feet washed, or give me the customary kiss. This woman, however, has washed my feet with her tears, and has not stopped kissing them."

He then turns to her and says, "Because of your great love and faith, all your many sins are forgiven. Go in God's peace."

Some of the guests start grumbling, "Who does he think he is, to be forgiving sins?"

When the dinner is over and we leave, I notice that the disciples walk in separate little groups. And I hear angry comments. I can tell that Simon, for one, is not happy about what has just happened.

That night, the disciples toss and turn, unable to get to sleep. And Jesus stays up a long time, with me on his lap. "Pup," he says, "I wish I could make everyone happy. But I have to speak the truth, and if that unsettles people, so be it."

The next morning, as we are getting up, John's followers come running into our camp, clearly distraught.

Jesus asks what's wrong, and they tell him that Herod has had John killed.

Jesus asks them how it came about, and this is what they tell him.

It was Herod's birthday. The royal court was celebrating; everyone was drinking heavily; and then Herod's stepdaughter danced in front of the whole party. Herod was so pleased by the dance that he swore he would give the girl anything she asked for. Her mother got her to ask for the head of John the Baptizer on a plate. Not wanting to lose face before his guests, Herod kept his promise and had John killed.

Jesus stands there a moment, fighting back tears, and then says, "Did you get to tell John about me?"

"Yes."

"And what did he say?"

With tears in their eyes, they answer, "He told us that no one can have anything good unless God gives it to them. He said, 'I've been saying all along—you've heard me—that I am not the Messiah, but the one sent ahead of him. He must become more prominent, while I become less so."

I see everyone—John's followers and Jesus' disciples and Jesus himself—cry together over the loss of John.

Then Jesus picks me up and we go off alone. The tears are running down his face and falling on me. As he pets me, he says, "Pup, this is more than the death of a cousin.

John unselfishly prepared the way for me. He gave all he had, including his life itself, out of faithfulness to his call from God. We have lost a loved one, and the world mourns the death of a prophet. But now he's going to be great in heaven."

I don't know what to do. Jesus holds me tight, and I feel that in some way I am helping him with his pain. It is good to be able to give back a little comfort to my Master.

10

"Give Them Something Yourselves"

The day after we hear of John's death, Jesus has us get into a boat and go to a quiet place to reflect on all that has happened. I hate boats. But evidently people don't, because a lot of them look to see where we're going and they get there ahead of us.

When Jesus sees them, he says to us, "These people have such faith! And they're in such need of sound teaching! I guess we'll have to put off our time of reflection until after we've helped them." And then he looks at me and says, "Pup, have you ever seen so many people? There must be thousands here."

As I walk beside Jesus, I notice lots who need healing, and it seems like everyone is asking for something.

After a long time of working with the people, Jesus turns to Philip and says, "It's getting late. I am afraid these folks will faint from hunger if we don't get them some food."

Philip says, "Well, we sure don't have the money to buy enough for this many people. Why not just send them on home for today?"

Jesus smiles and says, "I want you to give them something yourselves."

Then he says to Andrew, "Go find out if anyone has any food they could share."

A few minutes later, Andrew comes back and says, "I only found a boy who has five loaves of bread and two fishes. He's offered to share them, but how much help can this be?"

Jesus has him bring the boy to him, and he asks the boy if it is true that he has some food to share, and the boy nods.

Jesus says, "Why did you bring food?"

"Teacher," the boy says, "it's because my mother, knowing me, thought I might end up staying with you for a few days. She insisted that I bring a good amount of food."

Jesus says, "Are you sure you are willing to share this food that you might need for yourself?"

The boy looks deep into Jesus' eyes and says, "Everything I have is yours to do with as you wish."

Jesus smiles and takes the bread and the fishes. I jump up on the boy and lick his hand. I love kids anyway, but this one is really something.

Jesus asks everyone to be quiet and listen to him. Then he says, "This young boy has offered to share what little he has. Father, I ask that you bless this food, that we might all be nourished by it. And I also ask that you bless in a special way this boy. Even at his young age he has truly understood that the good news means sharing all the goods we have, both spiritual and material."

Having said this, he breaks the loaves and the fishes, gives them to the apostles, and tells them to give everyone as much as it takes to satisfy their hunger. The apostles look puzzled, but do as he says.

As they make their rounds, I notice a strange thing happening. No matter how many people take out of a basket some of the bread and fish, the amount left in the basket is not any less.

After everyone has had their fill, Jesus tells his helpers to gather up all the leftovers to give to the poor. And the leftovers fill up twelve whole baskets.

As these thousands of people leave, you can see that they are changed. When they came, some of them did need a healing of the body, but most of them needed their spirits healed. Jesus has healed them by sharing with them the good news. And he has done this mainly by showing them, with the help of a boy, that with the accepting of God's gifts comes the awesome privilege and responsibility of sharing these gifts with others.

The change can be seen in their faces. They are happy, and now know a little better how to treat one another.

When all of them have left, Jesus gathers our group together and says, "We still need some quiet time. I want you all to get in the boat and go to the other side of the lake. There we can be alone."

"Okay, Jesus," says Simon, "you get in the boat first, and we'll push it out into the water."

Jesus says, "Oh, no, you all go ahead. I'll meet up with you after I've finished some things I have to do."

Simon replies, "How will you catch up with us? It would be better for us to wait."

But Jesus says insistently, "No, you guys go on. Don't worry, I won't be long."

Then he picks me up and says, "You too, Pup—you go along in the boat," and hands me to John.

I don't like this. I want to be with my Master. And I am really not fond of boats in the first place. I try to get out. But Jesus stops me, saying, "Stay, Pup. You know I would never leave you unprotected. I'll be right behind you."

Simon has the others all get in the boat, and they start

rowing—and when we're about halfway across the lake, a big storm comes up, out of nowhere. The wind is awfully strong, the waves get higher and higher, and the boat is tossed and turned every which way. I'm scared to death. I look around, and see that most of the apostles are scared too. James, even though he's a fisherman, looks worried, and that makes me even more scared. Even Simon, who is at the helm, looks concerned. It's all he can do to keep us from capsizing.

All of a sudden Simon freezes and stares across the water. He points and shouts, "Look out there—what's that?"

Thaddaeus looks hard and says, "It looks like Jesus, walking on the water."

Simon snaps, "Don't be ridiculous; that's impossible."

But just then we hear Jesus' voice say, "Simon, it is me."

Simon is still not convinced. He says, "If it's really you, Jesus, then tell me to go out and meet you there."

Jesus reaches out his arms and calls back to him, "Come!"

Simon gets up, puts one foot over the side of the boat, and then stops and asks, "You really want me to come out to you?"

Jesus says, "Yes. Now!"

Finally Simon lets go and sets foot on the water, and to the amazement of us all, he does actually walk on it! And it must be a thrill, because he glances back at us as if to say, "Look! I'm walking on the water, just like Jesus!"

But just when he turns toward Jesus again, a gust of wind hits him in the face and water splashes up on him. This scares him, and he starts sinking.

He cries out to Jesus, "Save me!"

And Jesus reaches down, grabs him by the hand, and walks him to the boat, saying, "Simon, Simon, you have

NO LONGER A STRAY

so little faith. Why did you doubt? I told you I'd be here."

As they get into the boat, Jesus looks up at the sky and says, "Be still!" And then he looks down at the water and tells it, "Be calm!" And instantly the storm disappears.

Jesus sits down, and I run over and climb into his lap. I'm still trembling.

Jesus pets me and calms me down, saying, "Pup, you know that I'll always take care of you. You have nothing to fear. When I find a stray, whether you or anyone who will accept the good news, they become family to me and I take care of them."

He leans back and keeps rubbing my side. After a while he stops rubbing, and I know that he has fallen asleep. Then I notice the others talking. They're saying that they knew they were following someone great, *but* . . . "Who must Jesus really be," asks Thomas, "if even the wind and the waves obey his commands?"

No one ventures an answer to this question. They all go very quiet. But I know that Jesus is my Master, and really the Master of everyone and everything.

11

"Little Girl, Get Up"

It seems as if everyone is starting to realize that wherever my Master is, God is present.

Jesus sometimes looks at me and says, "Pup, we sure have a lot of people around us now, don't we?" And I think to myself, Yes, we sure do. There's hardly any place for me to lie down.

Today Jesus is teaching in the home of a friend. People are crowded into every little corner. I am lying under

Jesus' chair. Most of these people are accepting his message, but, as usual, some are there just to try to catch him making a mistake.

During his teaching I hear a commotion outside. I work my way to the front door, and I see four men carrying a man on a pallet. They tell Jesus' friend, "Our friend is paralyzed and we want Jesus to heal him."

Jesus' friend answers them, "There's no more room in my house. You'll have to see him some other time."

They say, "But we've come from so far away, and we care for our friend so much. We have to see the Teacher!" But he again says no, and comes back into the house.

A little later there's more commotion, but now it's coming from above. Everyone looks up and sees the ceiling being opened. The four men from outside lower the paralyzed man, with ropes that are tied to the corners of his pallet.

Jesus smiles and says to him, "Take heart, my son; your sins are forgiven you."

When he says this, some teachers of the Law whisper to one another, "That is blasphemy! Only God can forgive sins!"

I get up and growl.

Jesus puts his hand on my head, and says to them, "Why do you talk like this? Which is easier to say: 'Your sins are forgiven,' or 'Be healed'? But so that you know that I do have power to forgive sins"—he then looks at the man and says to him, "Get up, pick up your pallet, and go home."

Immediately, the man does as Jesus commands.

Most of the people are in awe. They say, "We have never seen anything like this!"

But the ones who have been accusing him of blasphemy now say to him, "If you have been empowered by God, why don't your disciples obey the fasting laws? They don't even observe the Sabbath properly! And they associate with known sinners!"

Jesus says, "Have you again forgotten what David and his followers did in time of need? All the laws you are quoting at me are meant to help bring people closer to God. The good news I am proclaiming is intended to get that across. But your rigid interpretation of the Law is suffocating people. My message is freeing."

Then he turns to me and the apostles and says, "I think it's time for us to move on." And on his way out he says to the others, "Those who hear the word of God and embrace it are already on the way to salvation."

As we walk down the road, Jesus says to me, "Pup, if those who consider themselves teachers and leaders of the people would only understand what accepting the good news could do, and give up their pride, they would win both the favor of God and the respect of the people."

But not all of the leaders are stubborn. One day, as we are walking down the road, one of the synagogue officials comes up to us, introduces himself as Jairus, and kneels down in front of Jesus. Because we've been having so many problems with these people, I go up to protect Jesus. But as I come up, I sense that Jairus is not an enemy, and I see that he is crying. In a trembling voice he says to Jesus, "My daughter is dying. I know that if you come and place your hands on her, she will live."

Jesus and Jairus and I immediately start walking toward Jairus' house, with the apostles and many others following. As the news spreads that Jesus has been asked to heal the official's daughter, the crowd grows.

On our way I notice a woman following Jesus and slowly getting closer to him. I move back to check her out, and I catch the smell of blood. She also looks very sick. I go back beside Jesus because I feel that she's no threat.

Suddenly Jesus stops and turns around. Then he asks, "Who just touched me, Pup?"

I look into the crowd, and see that woman looking down. But before I can point her out to Jesus, she comes up to him and says, "It was me, Lord. I've been sick for a long time, and I thought that if I could just touch your robe, I would get well. I'm sorry to trouble you."

"It's no trouble," Jesus says. "It was just that I felt the healing power go out from me. Your faith has made you well. Go in peace, healed of what has troubled you."

Even the apostles are amazed at this—that Jesus can sense power going out from him.

Shortly after that, someone comes up to Jairus and says, "I am so sorry to have to bring you this bad news. Your daughter has died."

Jairus cries out, "No!" and bursts into tears.

The messenger says to Jesus, "Teacher, thank you, but there is no longer any need for us to take up your time."

But Jesus puts his arm around Jairus and says, "Do not be distressed; continue to believe. We will go on to your house."

Outside the house, a lot of people have gathered to mourn the girl's death.

Jesus looks at them and says, "Why all the commotion and tears? The girl is not dead; she's only asleep."

They laugh and say, "You haven't even been in the house! You think we don't know death when we see it?"

After telling the apostles to keep the crowd out, he says, "Let's go in, Pup. Mom and Dad, you come too." And then he says, "Simon, James, and John, I also want you inside with us."

When we get in, I notice that the little girl is very pretty. Then I sniff at her, and I must admit, I do smell death about her. Maybe Jesus is wrong this time.

My senses tell me that she is dead. But I have seen Jesus do so many amazing things. Could he actually bring her back from death?

Jesus kneels down and takes the little girl by the hand. And then, in the same gentle voice that he used when he found me in the alley, he says to her, "Little girl, get up."

Nothing happens. Maybe there are some things he can't do.

Then he says, still very gently, "Please, little girl. Your parents love you so much. Bring joy back into their lives. Get up."

I hear her take a breath, and then I see her open her eyes. I quickly sniff her again. The smell of death is gone; I can only smell life in her.

Jesus turns to her parents and says, "Give her something to eat. And always treasure the gift that she is to you and your whole family. Enjoy the blessing that you have just been given. But don't tell anyone about it."

As we come out of the house, all the people gathered in front of it are looking at Jesus. They start to make fun of him again—but then the little girl shows up at the door, and they all fall silent.

Jesus turns to his followers and says, "I think we'd better move on. I'm afraid that the talk of this is going to be more than we want to handle right now. We need time to relax and pray."

We start down the road, Jesus and I in the lead, of course. Simon, James, and John tell the others all about what happened in the house. I can tell that some of them are having a hard time believing that the little girl was ever really dead. But I know that she had no life in her until Jesus asked her to get up.

Jesus picks me up and says, "Pup, it's so nice to bring happiness into a family. That little girl was so full of love, it would have been a shame not to give her the chance to share that love for many more years."

I lick his face. I, too, am happy that he brought her back to life. I love kids, and I could see that she was so innocent and giving.

Jesus continues, "There are some who will hate me for not letting her remain in the grip of death. They'll say that what I did was wrong. But how can I go wrong in doing the will of my Father? My Father tells me to spread the good news and bring love and joy into the world. And that's exactly what I just did. But I saw the faces of some of the people outside the house. I know this story will get twisted into something bad."

Jesus is right. Some only see him as a threat to their own selfish ends. What I see in him is love. Yes, my Master is all Love.

12

"You Must Let Go of Everything"

Whenever we stop, lots of people come around to listen to Jesus. Most of them find his message appealing, but we know there are always some who feel threatened by it and are there just to spy on Jesus, to catch him breaking a law. I'm most often the first one, after Jesus, to pick these people out. I can smell the ill will in them. It's hard to fool a dog.

Whenever I detect one of them, I growl and show my teeth. Jesus pats me on the head and says, "Pup, I know this is hard for you to understand, but I need to have those who consider me their enemy close at hand. They will help me show everyone the glory of God." But I still watch them very carefully.

One day, in Judea, we run into a group of Pharisees. They have that smell of evil about them. As they approach, I start to move forward. Jesus says, "Relax, Pup. Remember what I've told you." I back off, but only because it's what Jesus wants.

One of them—the one who smells the worst—says, "I have a question for you, Teacher."

Jesus nods.

This stinky one continues, "Is there any lawful reason for which a man can end his marriage and send his wife away?"

It's obvious from his tone of voice and the look on his face that he is just trying to trap Jesus. So Jesus answers, "Don't you know what Scripture says? That from the beginning the Creator 'made them male and female,' and that 'for this reason a man shall leave his father and mother and be joined to his wife, and the two shall become one flesh'?"

The Pharisee replies, "But Moses tells us, in the Law, that it is permissible."

"Yes," Jesus says, "but that is just because the people's hearts were so hardened against God's ways. I have come to perfect the Law, not water it down. If a man divorces his wife and marries someone else, he is committing adultery. To live in the world of the good news means having an unbreakable love—not looking for ways out, but, rather, working constantly at making stronger the love between husband and wife."

Bartholomew exclaims, "If that's the case—if marriage takes that much work and you can't get out of it, no matter what a pain she is—then a man would be better off not getting married at all!"

Jesus smiles and says, "God does call people to different lifestyles. Some are called to get married and teach their

NO LONGER A STRAY

children the way of the Lord. Others, for one reason or another, are incapable of taking on a married life. Some are born that way. Others are made that way by other people. And some choose a celibate life in response to a special call from God—let anyone take *this* who can! But in whichever way, in whatever group one finds oneself, one can and must fulfill God's plan and live fully the good news."

The crowd thins out; soon only some women and their children are left. Jesus and I are surrounded by kids. We are laughing and playing with them. It's been a long day, but both Jesus and I are happy to have the kids around. Jesus looks at me and says, "You know, Pup, we have not had this much fun since we called the others to join us. I've really missed being with children."

I notice then that Simon has called the mothers together and is talking to them. I don't like what I'm seeing, so I pull at Jesus' sleeve to call his attention to it.

Jesus calls out to Simon, "What are you telling them?"

Simon, looking a little sheepish, says, "I told them that you have been busy all day and need to rest, and so they should take their children and go home."

Jesus sighs deeply and says, "Simon, Simon! Can't you see how much these kids brighten my heart? This isn't work; it's play."

Then, turning to the other disciples, he says, "Unless you—all of you—accept me and the good news with as much innocence and openness as these little children do, none of you will ever meet me in heaven." And then he says to Simon, "Don't *ever* send the children away from me."

We go on playing with the kids for a long time. The disciples stay very quiet, but Simon is obviously upset.

When the children have all left, Jesus gathers the disciples together and says, "Don't miss the lesson I just taught you. Out of the mouths of the young can come great wisdom." And then, putting his arm around Simon, he says, "Simon, I know you had my best interest at heart. But this time you were wrong. I love you, but that doesn't mean I won't challenge you to grow. A rock cutter has to shape a stone to make it fit into the foundation. That's what I did for you today. Please don't let your anger get in the way of the good that can come of this incident." Jesus gives Simon a hug. I see Simon relax, and I know that everything is patched up between them.

A few days later, a young man comes up to the group. By his clothes I can tell that he is rich. He kneels before Jesus and says, "Teacher, what must I do to gain eternal life?"

Jesus tells him to get up, and then he says, "You know the commandments given by God to Moses. Keep these and you will live."

The man answers, "I have kept the commandments all my life. I feel drawn to do more."

Jesus looks deep into his eyes and says, "A man after my own heart! Son, if you want to follow God perfectly, go sell all that you have and give the money to the poor—that way you will have treasure in heaven—and then come follow me."

The man, looking sad, says, "Everything? I am a very wealthy man."

Jesus says, "You must let go of everything and only hold on to the truth of the good news."

The man turns around and slowly walks away.

Jesus looks at me and says, "Pup, I'm afraid that we won't be seeing him in our band of followers. And it's too bad. He would have gained so much more than he was giving up if he had only taken the chance and let go of it all."

Matthew comes up and asks, "What happened with that young man? Why did he go away?"

Jesus says, "He learned a very hard lesson, and could not accept the challenge."

"What lesson?" asks Matthew.

Jesus gathers the disciples around him so that they can all hear his answer.

He says, "You know that gate there is in a fortified city, the gate they call 'the needle's eye'?"

They nod.

"It's so narrow," he says, "that you can't get a camel through it without taking everything off of it and doing a lot of pushing and pulling. That way, nothing can be smuggled into the city. Well, it is easier for a camel to get through that needle's eye than for a rich person to get into heaven. The rich grasp at what they think is wealth. But that stuff is nothing compared to what they would gain by embracing the good news. They need to strip themselves of the worthless possessions of this world."

Thomas asks, "If that is the case, then who can be saved?"

Jesus answers, "It is impossible for anyone to be, except with the help of God."

Simon blurts out, "Look, Jesus, we've left everything. What will our reward be?"

Jesus says, "Anyone who has left home, family, or earthly wealth for the sake of me and the good news will be rewarded."

"But what does that really mean?" asks Simon.

Jesus explains, "Whatever you give up, you get blessed with a hundred times more of it. You give up a home, and your home becomes any place believers come together. You give up a family, and now every follower is your brother or sister. You share in everyone's blessings. Now, you do need to know that you will also suffer persecution. But pain is a part of life. Think of childbirth pain, which brings about such great joy. The pain you suffer on earth will bring you the joy of eternal life."

He pauses for a moment, and then adds, "And remember, we are here to serve, not to be served. It is in giving that we come to understand how blessed we are."

That night, all the disciples are discussing what Jesus has said and trying to figure out what it means. Jesus looks at me and says, "Come on, Pup. Let's let them chew on that bone for a while."

We go off by ourselves. Jesus sits down, and I climb up on his lap. He starts petting me, and says, "PupPup, I really was hoping that young man would join us. It's too bad he didn't have the courage to follow me." Then he motions over to the disciples and says, "I think this last lesson really has them confused. If they thought that following me was going to give them power or wealth, they were wrong! The wealth I offer is not of this world. And the power is in God."

I think to myself how much my life has changed since Jesus found me in the alley. The power I've been given is the love of Jesus. And the wealth is in being a follower of my Master.

13

"We Have Some Housecleaning to Do"

We're traveling to Jerusalem, and everyone is in a good mood. It's getting near festival time.

We stop to rest and have some lunch in a shady grove. It feels good to be out of the sun. I'm next to Jesus, having my belly rubbed.

All of a sudden we hear John say, "Mom! What a surprise!" His brother James jumps up and hugs their mother, saying, "What are you doing here?"

She says, "I heard you were in the neighborhood, and just wanted to see how you're doing."

Jesus gets up and gives her a hug. Then I go over to her, and she bends down, pats my head, and says, "You must be PupPup. I've been hearing so much about you. John likes you a lot."

Jesus invites her to join us for lunch. The other disciples come over and say hello, and then go back to where they were so that she can visit with her sons.

After she has eaten and rested, she says to Jesus, "I have a favor to ask of you."

Jesus smiles and says, "If I can help you, I'd be delighted to."

She says, "Promise me that in your kingdom my two sons will sit beside you, one at your right and the other at your left."

I look at James and John; they look embarrassed.

Jesus says to her, "You don't know what you're asking. Do you think that your sons can handle what is coming?"

She says, "Yes. Just ask them."

Jesus turns to them and asks, "Can you follow me all the way?"

The two get very serious and answer, "Yes, we can!"

Jesus says to them, "All right, you will be in on everything I am called to do. But it is not for me to assign the places in the Kingdom; that is for the One who sent me."

The rest, having heard part of this, gather around us. Simon, speaking for them all, says to James and John, "What makes you so special? Why should you get the places of honor? Maybe some of us are more deserving."

Jesus, looking disappointed, says, "Have you guys learned nothing? In this world riches, power, and status are thought to be important. To truly embrace the good news is to live in a whole different way—not wanting to be served, but, rather, striving to serve others, and sharing everything you have, with no thought of what you'll get back. Your reward is beyond this world."

They all look ashamed and move away.

When the mother of James and John gets up to leave, she says, "I'm sorry to have caused problems. I just wanted to take care of my sons."

Jesus smiles and says, "No one can blame you for that. And actually it just gave me a chance to make clearer to them what the good news is about." They all hug, and she leaves.

Then we leave the grove, too, and soon we come to the Mount of Olives, which is near Bethpage and Bethany. Jesus has us pause, and then he calls Thaddaeus and James Junior over and says to them, "Go into the village. There you'll find a little donkey which hasn't been ridden on yet. Untie it and bring it to me."

Thaddaeus asks, "What if someone stops us?"

Jesus says, "Just tell them that the Master has need of it. You'll have no problem."

When they return with the colt, they tell us, "It was just as Jesus said. The moment that we said the Master needs it, they blessed us and sent us on our way."

Jesus gathers everyone and says, "It's time for us to become bolder and shake up some people. The way we're going to enter Jerusalem this time will make our message very hard to ignore. But not everyone will be glad to see us." Getting onto the donkey, he says, "Let's see what happens."

I am running and barking alongside Jesus, and the

disciples are walking behind. Suddenly I'm hearing people shout, "Look! Jesus is coming!" And as we pass them, they join the procession.

Now it starts looking like a parade. People cover the road in front of Jesus with their cloaks and with leafy branches they've cut from the trees. They are waving their hands and calling out, "Praise to him who comes in the name of the Lord!" and "Hail, Son of David!" Everyone is excited. I run around the colt and bark with joy; that's my way of praising my Master.

When we get near the Temple, I see some Pharisees standing there. They are not joining in the shouts of praises. In fact, they look angry. I hear one of them grumble to another, "You can see that you're not getting anywhere. Look, the whole world has gone after him."

I plant myself between them and Jesus and show my teeth.

They call out to Jesus, "Teacher, tell them to be quiet! They are blaspheming!"

Jesus says, "I tell you, if they were to be quiet, the stones would shout the truth they proclaim. But it's getting late. We'll come back to the Temple tomorrow." Then, looking at me, he says, "Come on, Pup. This battle is not to be fought today."

The Pharisees look smug as the crowd disperses.

The next morning, we get up early to go to the Temple. Jesus is leading the way, and looking very determined. As usual, I'm right alongside him and the disciples are behind us.

When we arrive, Jesus stops and looks around. People are exchanging money and buying and selling all kinds of things. They are doing lots of haggling and swapping, showing no concern about the holiness of the Temple.

I've never seen Jesus look so mad. He picks up a rope

and makes a whip out of it, and then looks at me and says, "Pup, I think we have some housecleaning to do."

He strides into the Temple, with me right beside him. The disciples are hanging back, not knowing what is about to happen. He says loudly, in a tone of authority, "God has said, 'My house is to be a house of prayer,' but you are making it a den of thieves!" And then he starts chasing the sellers out and turning over their tables. I run around helping him, by pulling tables down and making everything fall off of them.

I see someone start to swing at Jesus' head with a club. I recognize him—this is a man who used to be mean to me when I was in the alleys. Now he is being mean to my Master. So I run up and bite that lowlife. He turns and swings at me, but misses. Jesus says, "Thanks, Pup!" I just bark and continue. The disciples are still just watching, not knowing what to do.

When all the sellers and money changers are gone, Jesus sits down, calls me over, and says, "Now, that's better, Pup." I bark in agreement and think to myself, I haven't had this much excitement since my days of stealing food from the markets. Only this time what I was doing was for the sake of God, not myself.

As the disciples look around at the mess, Jesus says to them, "I will not allow this Temple, this place dedicated to the One who sent me, to be made a scandal."

Once the Temple courtyard has been cleared out, poor people come in, and Jesus heals all who are sick or disabled.

When he is finished, we go back to our place of rest and talk about all that's happened. Jesus' disciples are amazed at how quickly he got angry, and also at how quickly he returned to his normal composure.

The next morning, when we arrive at the Temple, we

again run into Pharisees, teachers of the Law, and elders. I move up to protect Jesus, and he says to me, "Stand back, Pup; this will be no problem at all."

They ask him, "By what authority do you do such things as you did yesterday?"

He says, "I will ask you just one question, and if you answer it I will tell you where my authority comes from. Here's my question: Where did John's authority come from? From God, or from himself?"

They huddle together. I sneak up to hear what they're saying. One of them says, "If we say God, he will ask us why we haven't accepted John's call to repent." Another one says, "Yes, but if we say it was from himself, then we'll have trouble with the people, because they honor John as a great prophet."

They turn back to Jesus and say, "We don't know."

Jesus says, "Fine. Then neither will I tell you where my authority comes from."

He slowly turns and walks away, and we all follow.

That night, after all the rest have gone to sleep, Jesus says to me, "Come on, Pup, we need to pray." We go off by ourselves, and he picks me up and holds me.

"Pup," he says, "what I said at the Temple today is going to make them anxious to get rid of me. Today we have made some real enemies. But those who don't accept the good news were already seeing us as enemies."

He starts rubbing my ear and prays, "Father, these last few days have made us very visible. We have had some good times, but I know that very hard times are coming. Those who are with me need your strength to endure. I also need your fatherly love."

Then he looks at me and says, "Oh yes, also give Pup extra strength."

I think to myself, I love Jesus so much! And how much

he must love me! He is asking God to help *me*. But as long as I have my Master, why would I need extra strength?

14

"I Think You Are Ready"

By this time our little band is not so little. The twelve apostles are, of course, always with Jesus and me. But others have also begun to stay with us. Some stay for only a little while, but others are always with us.

As usual, Jesus is up early, watching the sunrise and talking to God. And as always, I am with him. This morning he picks me up and starts rubbing my ear. He only does this when he is sorting out a problem.

"Pup," he says, "time is growing short. We need to get the good news out to more people. The disciples need some experience in spreading our teaching. It's time to do some delegating."

After breakfast, Jesus calls all of his followers together. There must be over a hundred people—men, women, even some whole families. Jesus asks them to sit down and listen carefully.

"The Twelve have been with me the longest," he says. "But some of you others have by now been following me long enough to take on some of the responsibility of spreading the good news. The message that I bring is not something one should keep to oneself; it is something to be shared."

One of those other followers says, "So, you are going to send out the Twelve and have us take over the responsibilities of the camp?"

"No," says Jesus. "I did once before send out the Twelve to spread the good news, and they did a fine job. But this time I need them with me; we need to prepare for our next trial. So I'm going to be sending you out to the neighboring towns, to teach the people."

Someone else gets up and says, "Teacher, do you really think we are ready to take on such a task?"

Jesus smiles and says, "If you have taken the message into your heart, you are ready. If you are only mouthing the good news, then this will be a test that you won't make it through. But I think you are ready. It will not be easy, but I have confidence in you."

Another one says, "You don't think I'm too young? I'm scared. How exactly are we to spread the good news?"

Jesus says, "I'm going to send you out in twos. That way you'll each have a companion to support you. For this is not going to be an easy task. At times you will feel like a lamb surrounded by a pack of wolves. But use the same method that the Twelve used. Go to the towns that I plan on stopping at, and prepare the way for me. Travel light; carry as little money and clothing as possible; that way you can move quickly. Don't get distracted along the way; the time is short. When you come to a town, go to the first house you see, and give the greeting, 'Peace to this household!' If there's someone there who is open to the good news, your peace will rest on that person. But if not, it will come back to you, and you should move on. At whatever house you do stay in, accept the food and drink you are offered, and don't feel indebted; it is a worker's pay. And don't search around for a better place; stay where you are first invited to stay. If, after hearing the good news, the people there reject it, then leave that place, shaking the dust from your feet. They will have chosen their own judgment from God."

After saying this, Jesus has the Twelve join him, and they ask these others to stand and get ready to be sent on their mission.

Jesus prays, "Father, I ask that you bless and strengthen these whom we send out. Open their minds and mouths to preach the good news which you have given them through me."

Then he has the Twelve go and bless them individually and send them out in twos.

When they have left, and we are back to our little band, Bartholomew asks, "Why didn't we get to go with them?"

Jesus gathers everyone around and says, "I need you with me for what is about to happen. But remember that the good news is always to be spread, not kept hidden. In the future you will find that you will have to send out others to continue the work I've started with you."

I look at their faces and see a lot of confusion. Jesus sees it too, and just says, "You'll understand later, trust me."

When we leave the place where we have been staying, Jesus picks me up and carries me. I'm wondering why he is doing this, and then he says, "Pup, I am happy to be sending out our followers, but I also sense storms gathering. That's why I've kept with me those who have seen the power of God. They may be able to understand something of what is about to happen, though it will cause them pain. And you—I'm afraid you will also have to go through a lot of pain, but I want you to know that my love will always be with you."

I lick his face in thanks, but I wonder what he is talking about. And I'm a little afraid.

▲▼▲▼▲

One day, as we're walking along, Jesus says, "I have some friends in the area—let's stop at their place to rest." This is in Bethany.

When we get to the house, a man comes to the door, looks out, and says, "Well, bless my soul!" Then he turns around and says to the others in the house, "Look who has come to visit us!"

Right away two women come to the door and say, together, "Jesus! Welcome to our home!" They and the man come outside. I run up to greet them, and the younger woman bends down and starts petting me. The older one seems a little embarrassed about something.

Jesus asks, "Would it be all right for my friends and me to rest here for a little while before we go on?"

They all say, "Sure! We'd be delighted."

Jesus introduces the apostles by name, and then says, "And Mary, the one you're spoiling is PupPup." To the apostles he says, "These are my very good friends Lazarus and his sisters Martha and Mary."

Martha, the older woman, says, "Now, Jesus, you've caught me off guard. I'm sorry to say, all I've got prepared is a simple lunch."

Jesus says, "We weren't expecting anything; we just need some rest and a little water."

Martha says, "Oh, no, you will not shame me by not letting me show you proper hospitality." She goes in the house, and soon we hear a lot of activity in the kitchen.

Lazarus says, "I'm afraid you won't get out of here without having had a real meal. While you wait, have something to drink and tell us what you've been doing."

We sit down in the shade. I stay next to Mary, who has not stopped petting me and rubbing my belly. Jesus smiles at me and says, "Pup, you're really eating up all this attention, aren't you?" I wag my tail.

Jesus tells Lazarus and Mary about all that's been happening—the blessings and the troubles—and they listen with great interest, asking questions and making comments.

At one point Lazarus says, "I've been hearing that you

are shaking up some of our power-obsessed leaders. I'm proud to call you my friend."

A little later, Martha comes out, carrying a lot of food and saying to Jesus, "Will you look at that lazy girl! She's doing nothing but sit around and listen to your stories and pet that dog!"

I look up, not happy that my new friend is being attacked.

Martha continues, "She's left me to do all the work of preparing the meal!"

Jesus looks at her and says gently, "Martha, Martha, I told you that all we needed was a little rest and water. You were the one to decide to make a fuss over us. We appreciate what you're doing, but Mary doesn't want to miss a word of what I am saying, and I will not deprive her of the opportunity to share in our mission. She has chosen the better course."

Martha looks a little hurt, but Mary does get up to help her.

Then everyone lends a hand in setting the table, and we enjoy a pleasant meal together.

When Jesus sees that everyone has finished eating, he stands up and says, "Well, it's time to go. Thank you so much for everything." He hugs all three of these friends, and then says to Martha, "I hope you're not put out with me for what I said."

She says, "Of course not. You're probably right. I always want everything to be perfect. Maybe next time I'll be calmer. I need to learn to listen more and be less concerned about the less important things."

Now we're back on the road, refreshed. Everyone is in a good mood. We haven't had much trouble in the past few days.

When we stop for the night and are sitting around the

fire, Jesus says, "I wonder how those we sent out are doing. I expect them back soon. I'm sure they are touching many people with their sharing of the good news."

Little by little, the others drop off to sleep. Once again it's Jesus and me. He holds me and says, "Pup, it's days like this, with you and other friends, that I'm going to miss the most."

Tonight he falls asleep holding me. I think to myself: What is he talking about, "miss the most"? He can't leave me. Where would I be without my Master?

15

"That Is How You Are to Pray"

When we travel we're always followed by a lot of people, but this doesn't bother me, since I'm always running ahead of the group.

We are near the cities of Tyre and Sidon when all of a sudden I hear a woman shout, "Son of David, take pity on me!"

I stop and look around, but Jesus just keeps walking, so I ignore her.

Then, even more loudly, she shouts, "Please, sir! My daughter has a demon and is in a terrible state!"

I notice that she looks different from all the other people I've met.

When I run back to Jesus, I hear Judas say, "Teacher, get rid of her—give her what she wants so she'll go away. She's disturbing everyone with her shouting."

I growl at Judas, because Jesus doesn't get rid of anybody. But Jesus looks at me and says, "Pup, be quiet. You're being as judgmental as Judas."

I look hurt, but actually am ashamed, because I know that what Jesus has said to me is right.

Jesus says to Judas, "I was sent only to the lost sheep of the house of Israel."

But the woman comes up to Jesus, falls at his feet, and says, "Help my daughter, sir!"

Jesus looks at her and says, "Let the children be fed first. It is not fair to take the children's bread and throw it to puppies."

When I hear that, I whimper. Jesus looks at me, and so does the woman. And then she answers, "That is true, sir, but the puppies under the table do get the children's crumbs."

Jesus picks me up and hugs me, and then looks at her with a gentle smile and says, "You are a woman of great faith! What you have asked for is done. Go back to your daughter."

She throws her arms around his legs and thanks him over and over. Then she gets up and rushes home.

Some days later, Jesus and I are returning from our morning prayer, and as we are coming over to the disciples and some other people who have come to hear Jesus teach, a man calls out to him, "Teacher, have pity on my son!"

Jesus asks, "What's wrong with your son?"

The man answers, "He is plagued by a speechless spirit. Wherever it seizes him, it dashes him down; and he foams at the mouth, grinds his teeth, and goes stiff. I asked your disciples to cast it out, but they were not able to."

Jesus exclaims, "You faithless, perverse generation! How long will I be with you? How long do I have to put up with you? Bring the boy to me."

As they are leading the boy to Jesus, he falls on the ground and starts rolling around and foaming at the mouth. This really scares me, so I hide behind Jesus.

Jesus looks at me and says, "Come on, Pup, *you* believe in me, don't you?"

I wag my tail and come out from behind him, but am still a little nervous.

Jesus asks the boy's father, "How long has he been like this?"

The father answers, "Ever since he was little. He has often thrown himself into fire or water. Have pity on us and help us, if you can."

Jesus says, "'If you can'? Everything is possible for a person with faith!"

The father cries out, "I do have faith—just not enough! Cure my lack of it!"

By this time the crowd has grown, and is starting to move in closer.

Jesus stoops down and says in a loud voice, "I order you to leave this boy and never return!"

Suddenly the boy lies still. To everyone he looks dead. But I run up and sniff him, and I recognize the smell of life, not death.

Jesus says, "Pup, wake him up." So I nudge him with my nose, and then grab his sleeve and pull on it, and he opens his eyes and gets up.

Jesus turns to the man and says with a twinkle in his eye, "I guess your faith deficiency has been remedied?"

The man nods, and thanks Jesus, and takes his son home.

At the end of the day Thomas asks, "Why couldn't we drive the evil spirit out of that boy?"

"Because you didn't have enough faith to pray," says Jesus. "The spirit was of a kind that can only be gotten out by prayer. I assure you that if you had faith even the size of a mustard seed, you could say to this hill, 'Move to over there!' and it would. It is with faith, self-denial, and prayer that you will be able to harness the power of the good news."

Jesus and I go off for our night prayer. He sits down and prays while watching the sunset. I am curled up next to him.

When he is finished praying, he lifts me up onto his lap and starts petting me, and says, "You know, Pup, I think my disciples are a little upset with me for telling them that the reason they couldn't heal that boy was that they didn't have enough faith. But I have to speak the truth. And they will learn that faith is like a muscle—the more you use it, the stronger it gets. I'm sure they'll get over it."

Yes, I think to myself, today even I slipped backward and hid behind Jesus. But it won't happen again. Never again will I doubt Jesus. No matter how scared I get, I will stand by my Master.

A day or two later, when we are sitting around the fire at night and Jesus and I are playing, Andrew says, "Excuse me, Jesus, I want to ask you a favor. Would you mind teaching us how to pray? When I was with your cousin John, he taught us something about that, and it made our lives so much easier."

Jesus says, "No, I don't mind at all. In fact, I've been waiting to be asked."

Then he calls me over, saying, "Pup, come and lie down next to me and rest, as I teach my disciples how to be in touch with God in prayer." And of course I happily do this. Because I have been with him so often at prayer time, I almost feel like I could do this teaching myself.

Jesus smiles and says, "When you pray, don't be like the hypocrites! They love to stand up and pray in the houses of worship and on the street corners, so that everyone will see them. I assure you, they have their reward. But when you pray, go into your room and shut the door—go off somewhere by yourself—and pray, unseen, to your Father, who is unseen. That way you will not be distracted from your Father, who is always with you. And when you pray, don't use a lot of meaningless words like the pagans, who think that God will be made more receptive by the length of their prayer. Your Father already knows what you need before you ask."

They all nod in agreement.

Then Philip says, "It is so simple. Why do the Pharisees make it so difficult?"

"I don't know," says Jesus, "but let me give you a good example of a prayer that is pleasing to God."

He pauses, and then, looking up to the heavens, he says, "Our Father in heaven, may your name be revered, your kingdom come, your will be done, on earth as in heaven. Give us today our daily bread, and forgive us the wrongs we have done you, as we forgive others the wrongs they have done us. And do not expose us to temptation, but free us from all evil."

Then he looks at them and says, "That is how you are to pray. In praying like that, you praise and thank God and show him that you believe in him and accept your responsibility as a believer."

I notice that there is a real feeling of closeness in the group right now.

When Jesus is done speaking, Andrew walks over to him, sits down beside him, and says, "Thank you for letting us share in your relationship of having God as Father."

Jesus gets up, and so do all the apostles. Everyone is smiling and saying good night to each of the others. Even I am getting something special—extra pats on the head.

When everyone has settled down, Jesus looks at me and says, "I think that will take the place of our night prayer, to end this day. Let's go to sleep, PupPup."

I lie down beside Jesus, and he slowly rubs my ear. Just before I drop off to sleep, I think to myself, Did he really mean to give every human being a claim on being a son or daughter of God? And I think about how living the good news makes all people brothers and sisters of my Master.

16

"Who Really Is My Family?"

One day we're on the shore of Lake Gennesaret, and of course a large crowd gathers around us, and of course it includes some teachers of the Law and some Pharisees—but this time they are right up front. This does not make me very happy. I sense trouble coming.

I jump up on Jesus' leg to warn him, and I feel tension there. Now I am worried!

Before I can do anything, one of the Pharisees calls out to Jesus, "Teacher, we want to see a miracle! This will prove to us that you are truly sent by God."

Jesus groans, shakes his head, and then says, "You godless hypocrites. No! You will not witness miracles. You are only open to what you want to see. I tell you, on Judgment Day the people of Nineveh will be witnesses against you, because they learned from Jonah and gave up their sinful ways. And the Queen of Sheba will accuse you, because she traveled all the way from her country to listen to the wisdom of King Solomon. Look! Here in your midst is something greater than Jonah or Solomon."

Now they are so angry, they cannot speak. They clench and raise their fists, and the other people step aside. But all this excitement brings even more people to the shore.

I'm still standing beside Jesus when suddenly I pick up a familiar scent. Can it really be Mary, his mother? I can hardly believe it. I make my way through the crowd, and sure enough it is her, with a number of their relatives. When I rush up she bends down and picks me up. Holding me close, she says, "It's been a long time, Pup. How are things going?"

I think to myself, Actually things are getting a bit scary. But I know that Jesus is going to be so happy to see her. And it will make him feel so much better.

Just then I hear someone call out to him, "Teacher! Your mother and family are at the back of the crowd. They want to see you."

Jesus does not look at his family. Instead, he looks at the crowd and says, "Who really is my family?"

I look at Jesus in amazement. I can't believe what I'm hearing.

He says, "Anyone who accepts the good news that I bring, and does the will of my Father in heaven, that person is my brother and sister and mother."

I quickly turn and look at Mary. Her eyes are shiny, but there is also a look of understanding. She puts me down, and says, "PupPup, go back to Jesus. He is right, this is not the time for us to be with him. Although letting go hurts terribly, we cannot hold him back from this mission that the angel told me about before he was born. He no longer belongs to us. Now he is family to all who accept his call. We will wait and see him later, when he is finished preaching."

Mary and the other relatives turn and walk away. I notice that they do not look back. I think it would be too hard for them. They are sacrificing so much, though it is for the good of so many.

I come back to Jesus, and he picks me up. I look him in the face, so he can see how sad I am, and he holds me close and says, "I know, Pup; I saw them. But it is too dangerous for Mom and the family to be around me. As you can see from what happened today with those teachers and Pharisees, things might start getting a little rough. I don't want Mom too to suffer that right now. She will have more than enough to suffer later."

I lick his face, knowing now that he sent them away out of concern for her. And it did give him a chance to let everyone know something wonderful: that accepting the good news creates a bond stronger than blood.

By now the crowd is so big and thick that it is pushing in on us. Everyone wants more information about the good news.

Jesus says to the crowd, "Give me a moment. I want to get in the boat with my disciples and move out a little from the shore, so that you can all hear. Then I will give you the next lesson."

He gets into the boat, still holding me. I wish he would stop using boats—I still don't like them, although I am getting more used to them.

As the boat moves out a few yards, the people sit down on the shore.

Jesus begins by saying, "Listen well!"

Then he puts me down and tells this story: "Once there was a farmer who went out to sow grain. When he scattered the seed, some of it fell along the path, where it was stepped on, and then eaten up by birds. Some of it fell on rocky ground, and so when the plants sprouted they dried up, because the soil had no moisture. Some of the seed fell among thorn bushes, which grew up with the plants and choked them. But some of it fell on good soil, and the plants grew and bore grain—a hundred grains each."

Then, after a brief pause, he says in a loud voice, "Those who wish to understand this parable should come and ask me about it."

We move a little further from the shore and drift out into the lake. I look back, and see many people talking. Some seem fascinated by what Jesus has said, but others seem less interested.

Jesus is sitting in the front of the boat and enjoying a little peace and quiet with the apostles. I am sitting on his lap. That is the only way I feel safe in a boat.

Bartholomew breaks the silence. He asks, "Why do you so often use parables?"

The others all nod; clearly they are wondering the same thing.

He says, "The gift of understanding is not given to all people in the same way, and acceptance also varies. Many people close their ears, only hearing what they want to hear. Others are indifferent, and don't respond. The challenge is to open up in mind and heart to truly understand the message in all its depth."

I look at the apostles, and they seem very interested in what Jesus is saying. This fills him with an excitement that seemed to have been drained out of him when we were on the beach with the teachers and Pharisees. He picks me up and puts me down in the bottom of the boat, saying to the apostles, "Let me show you what I mean."

His intensity is so great, and by now I feel so safe, that I don't even mind not being held.

He says, "This is what the parable means. The seed is the word of God. The path is the people who hear it but do not understand it. The Evil One comes and snatches it away from them. The rocky ground is those who hear it and gladly welcome it, but do not let it take root in them. As soon as trouble comes, they turn away from God. The thorn bushes are those who hear and accept it, but then become distracted by worldly worries, riches, and pleasures. These things choke out the word of God. The good ground is those who hear and really take to heart the truths proclaimed by God. These people are rewarded beyond all their dreams."

Matthew says, "So the seed is the good news you have been imparting to us."

Jesus says, "Yes! Go on."

Philip says, "The farmer is you, right?"

Jesus smiles and says, "Yes. And what else?"

John says, "You're inviting us to be the good ground and take in all that you are telling us and pass it on to many others. Right?"

Jesus, looking very happy, says, "Yes! I am proud of all of you." Then he scoops me up and says, "Now, Pup, you see that I did choose the right ones to help me with the mission that God my Father gave me."

We are all happy and enjoying being together. There's lots of kidding and teasing and laughing going on. The mood has certainly changed from what it was a few hours ago. It's as if Jesus' followers have passed a big test.

Jesus invites me back up on his lap and says, "Pup, it makes my day when I see people really begin to understand how much God loves everyone. Especially when it is those who are with me and have become family to me. God is not vengeful; he is all loving."

While he scratches my ear, he looks up and quietly says a little prayer: "Thank you, for opening their minds and helping them understand things." And in my heart I also thank God, for letting me be found by Jesus, my loving Master.

17

"He Would Give You Living Water"

As we travel, the crowds keep getting larger. Often the reason is just curiosity to see Jesus and his band of followers. It is evident that more and more people are talking about my Master.

It is especially evident when we get to Jericho. The streets are solidly lined with people. As we walk by, many of them loudly cheer. The spies are also there, of course, but they just watch, saying nothing.

I'm running in front, as I often do, and all of a sudden I see a man in a tree. I don't know why anyone would be in a tree, but this could be someone who wants to hurt Jesus, so I stop and bark at him.

Jesus comes up to me and says, "Quiet, Pup—his house is where we'll be staying tonight."

Then Jesus says, "Zacchaeus! Come down—I want to talk to you."

Zacchaeus looks surprised, but comes down. And when he comes over to Jesus, I notice that although he is a grown-up, he is the size of a child.

Jesus asks him, "What were you doing up in that tree?"

Zacchaeus says, "As you can see, I am not a tall guy. I've heard of you, and I wanted to see you, but no one would let me through, so I had to climb up in that tree."

Jesus smiles and says, "Your persistence is to be rewarded. Would you be so kind as to let us stay with you for the night?"

Zacchaeus, surprised and thrilled as he clearly is, just says very simply, "With great pleasure. My house is your house."

Those who have heard this exchange start murmuring, saying, "How can Jesus, if what he is preaching is really good news, invite himself to the home of this notorious sinner, the chief tax collector?"

I notice that Zacchaeus hears these comments, and is hurt by them.

After we arrive at his home and get settled in for the night, Jesus asks, "Zacchaeus, did you hear what those people were saying?"

"Yes," he answers, "but look, Lord, I will give half of all that I have to the poor, and if I have extorted anything from anyone, I will repay it four times over."

Jesus says to us, "Today salvation has come to this house, and it's because this man too is a descendant of Abraham. The Son of Man came to seek and to save the lost."

That night, when we are about to drop off to sleep, Jesus holds me and says, "Pup, Zacchaeus is small in stature, but he has a very big heart. God is pleased with him. Those who hate him are the ones who are in conflict with God's will."

The next morning we start out early, because we have a long way to go.

At about noon we stop outside Sychar, which is a Samaritan town. Jesus is tired, so he asks his disciples to go into the town and buy the food we'll be needing. They set out. We sit down to rest, in the shade of a well.

But the noonday sun is very hot, and soon I am panting. Jesus looks at me and says, "Pup, I think you and I could use some water."

Just then a woman comes walking to the well, carrying a jug. Jesus asks her, "Could you please get us some water?"

She looks at Jesus like he's crazy and says, "How is it that you, a Jew, are asking a drink from me, a woman of

Samaria? You people won't have anything to do with us; you won't even use the same dishes as us."

Jesus says, "If you only knew who it is that is asking you to give him a drink, you would be the one asking, and he would give you living water."

She says, "Sir, you don't have a bucket, and the well is deep. So, where would you get this living water? Are you greater than our father Jacob, who gave us the well and drank from it himself with his sons and his cattle?"

Jesus says, "Whoever drinks the water that I will give will never again be thirsty. It will become in that person a spring of water welling up to eternal life."

I am watching all this, and wondering why Jesus is speaking in such a confusing way.

The woman puts down the jug and says, "Sir, give me that water, so that I won't have to keep coming to this well day after day."

Jesus says, "Go get your husband."

She looks down and says, "I don't have a husband."

Jesus gently smiles and says, "You are right in saying that you don't have a husband. You have had five husbands, and the man you are living with now is not your husband. You have told me the truth."

She sits down and says, "I can see that you are a prophet. Our ancestors worshiped God on this mountain; but you people say that Jerusalem is the place where one ought to worship."

Jesus smiles and says, "Actually, the time is coming when God will be worshiped in all places; when, by the power of his Spirit, people will worship the Father in the way he wants them to, which is by accepting the good news and living it."

The woman says, "I know that the Messiah is coming, and that when he comes he will explain everything."

Jesus says in a tone of authority, "I am he—I who am speaking to you."

The woman gasps.

Just then the disciples come back. They are clearly surprised to see Jesus talking alone with a woman; and as they get closer she walks away, leaving her water jug behind.

They give Jesus something to eat, but do not mention the woman. I am wondering why she went away so quickly.

In a short time she's back, with a lot of people who want to meet Jesus.

One of the men in this crowd asks him, "Are you the one she was talking to? She claims that you told her everything about her life, and that you are the Messiah."

Jesus nods and says, "Yes, I am. These are my followers. We are spreading the good news that will give everlasting life."

They say, "Please stay with us and share this gift with us."

Jesus turns to the disciples and says, "It's only right that the good news be given to any who desire it. We'll stay here a while and share our message with them."

That night, after Jesus prays, he says to me, "Pup, I am so glad that woman had the courage not to run from us, and was open enough to listen to someone different from her. Because of her, many of her people will be saved."

Two days of him being with them is all it takes; lots and lots of them come to believe. I hear several of them happily say to the woman, "It is no longer because of your words that we believe, for we have heard for ourselves, and we know that this is indeed the Savior of the world."

Near the end of the second day, we see a large group of people coming down the road. At first I don't recognize them, but when they get closer I pick up a familiar scent. It is those disciples that Jesus sent to spread the good news to other towns. I run to them, barking a greeting, and they all shout, "Look! PupPup is welcoming us back!"

When they reach the place where we're staying, there are lots of greetings and hugs.

Finally Jesus asks, "And how did your mission go?"

They say, "Great!" And then one of them adds, "Lord, even the demons submit to us when we use your name!"

Jesus says, "Yes, I know. I saw Satan fall like lightning from the sky. All of you listen: I have given you the power to tread down snakes and scorpions and the full force of the Enemy and not suffer any harm."

They all get very quiet, and then Jesus continues, "But do not rejoice in this, that the evil spirits submit to you. Rather, rejoice that your names are written in heaven."

The rest of the night, we sit around and enjoy being filled in on the experiences of one another's missions.

When all is quiet, Jesus and I go for our nightly time of prayer. This night, Jesus prays a very long time. I stay by his side, talking to God in my own way.

Finally Jesus picks me up and, holding me close, says, "Pup, things are moving so fast now. God certainly is showing to what extent the good news is about love. It's to the extent that he actually sent me, his Son, into the world to save it from its selfishness, sensualism, and pride."

Then Jesus gets very quiet. I sense that he is thinking about what the future will bring. He holds me tight, and I can feel his love.

I also sense some fear in him. But what does he have to fear? I just heard him refer to himself as God's Son. My Master, God's Son, what can there be for you to fear?

18

"I Will Now Tell You What You Are"

Jesus has taken us to a quiet place in the mountains, close to the town of Caesarea Philippi. We are there to relax, pray, and have time to grow closer. And everyone is relaxed and laughing. The others all take turns preparing the food and cleaning up, and I get to spend a lot of time playing; someone or other is always throwing a stick for me to fetch.

But my favorite time is at night, when we are all sitting around the fire. I always have my head on Jesus' lap, and he is constantly petting me.

On our first night there he looks at me and says, "Pup, this is really nice, isn't it? Look how close we have all become. I really like all the people who have accepted my call. Each one is different, but I love all of them so much."

I wag my tail and lick his hand. But deep inside I know that I don't love all of them so much. Some of them are scary, especially the Zealot.

I do love John very much—he's the youngest, and the one who takes the best care of me. If Jesus is busy with something, he's the one I go to.

But then there is Simon. I still can't figure out why Jesus asked him to join him. He is like a bull charging at anything that moves. I don't believe he really thinks out anything.

One night, as we are sitting around the fire, Jesus asks all the apostles, "What are the people saying about me? Who do they think I am?"

They give different answers.

Andrew: "Some think that you are John the Baptizer, back from the dead."

Matthew: "Some say Elijah."

Philip: "Jeremiah, or one of the other prophets."

Then Jesus says very seriously, "And you? Who do *you* think I am?"

They all get very quiet, and then suddenly Simon jumps up. I think to myself, Oh, this should be good—I bet he's going to make a fool of himself again.

In a strong, powerful voice, he says, "You are the Messiah, the Son of the living God!"

I am amazed, and he looks like he is too, at what just came out of his mouth.

Jesus jumps up, grabs his shoulders, and says, "Very good, Simon, son of John! The truth you have spoken was revealed to you by none other than my Father in heaven. So I will now tell you what you are: You are the rock on which I will build my church! I am making you the foundational support for the spreading of the good news."

Then he turns to the other apostles and says to them, "From now on, he will be called Peter—the Rock. His rocklike strength will help you get through any trials in the future."

Simon—I mean Peter—looks embarrassed by what Jesus has said.

The others all get up and hug him. But I still hang back.

Then Jesus looks at me and says, "Go on, Pup. He is now Peter, and I think you will find him a changed man."

Peter looks at me and says, "I guess I have given you a hard time, Pup. Let's forgive and forget, okay?"

He bends down and rubs my head. It's a little rougher than the way Jesus does it, but I do feel a change in him. I feel how much he loves and is committed to Jesus and the good news. I wag my tail and lick his hand; we're fine.

That night, we all celebrate the new closeness that we all feel.

▲▼▲▼▲

A few nights later, the atmosphere around the campfire gets much less cheerful.

Jesus makes sure all of the apostles are there; he says there are some things he needs to tell them. I have my head on his lap, and I can feel fear and sadness in the way he is petting me.

Sounding very sad, he says, "Soon we will be going to Jerusalem. There I will suffer much from the elders, the chief priests, and the teachers of the Law. They will bring trumped-up charges against me, and convict me, and have me put to death."

For a few moments everyone sits in stunned silence.

Then Peter gets up and says, "God forbid, Lord! No way will this ever happen to you!"

Jesus says, "Sit down, Peter! Now you are not saying something from God, but rather Satan is using you to tempt me away from my mission. Do not be afraid, because on the third day I will bring glory to God my Father by rising from the dead. All of my followers will be tested. Whoever is ashamed of me and my message, I will be ashamed of when I come as Son of Man in my Father's glory. But those who courageously take up their crosses and follow me, embracing the good news, I will proudly acknowledge before my Father."

I can see that this really gets the disciples thinking.

That night, everyone tosses and turns, unable to stop thinking about what Jesus has said.

Jesus picks me up and we go off by ourselves. "Pup," he says, "I know that I was blunt with them, but they need to know what is ahead of us. I want them to be committed to the good news with their eyes open."

Then he sits down, and we spend most of the night

together. Jesus just keeps petting me. I think he wishes he had not had to tell them about the future. I also think he's wishing that it would not be necessary for him to go through all those terrible things he told us about.

▲▼▲▼▲

On our last day in the mountains, Jesus says, "Come on, Pup, I need to do some praying. I want to go further up on this mountain."

He looks around for a moment, and then says, "Peter, James, and John, you come too. I think it would be good for you to go up this mountain with me to pray."

It is a hard climb up the mountain.

When we get to the top, Jesus says, "Find a place for being with God."

Jesus and I go a little closer to the edge. I lie down, and he starts praying. I feel very strongly the presence of God. I look around to see if the other three have the same feeling—and they have fallen asleep! This makes me a little mad. I decide to wake them up.

But just as I get to my feet, I notice that something is happening on the mountain. The light is getting brighter, and there is a rush of wind. The three disciples wake up, and the looks on their faces tell me that something is happening to Jesus.

I quickly turn around, and there he is, standing in the middle of a cloud. Two men I have never seen before are with him, one on each side, talking to him. I don't know what to do.

Then I hear Peter say to the other two disciples, "Elijah and Moses are here! But that can't be, can it?"

Then he says to Jesus, "It *is* good for us to be here! Do you want us to put up tents for the three of you?"

There is a rumbling of thunder as he finishes speaking.

Then this thunder becomes the same voice we heard at the Jordan River, when Jesus was with John the Baptizer.

When the disciples hear the voice, they fall to the ground in terror and hide their faces.

The voice says, "This is my Son, the Chosen One. Listen to him."

After this, everything is back the way it was, but the disciples still have their faces to the ground. Jesus comes up to them and says with a smile, "You can get up; you have nothing to fear. I want you to remember everything that has happened on this mountain, but it's for the strengthening of your faith. Don't tell anyone about it until after I have risen from the dead."

We go back to the camp. When we walk in, Peter and James and John remain silent, but the others can tell, just by looking at their faces, that something has happened. Jesus brings everyone around and just says, "It's time to go back to spreading the good news."

Jesus and I lead the others out of the mountains. The disciples are in little groups, talking. Peter, James, and John cannot get over what they experienced on the mountaintop with Jesus, Moses, and Elijah.

This time away has made us more committed to Jesus' good news, but it has also opened our eyes to what is expected of us. Jesus looks down at me and says, "Pup, that was a very blessed time together. Not only have you finally accepted Simon, the one we are now calling Peter, but also I can see that our little band is ready to proclaim the good news without fear. Remember, Pup, each of you has freely agreed to follow me. We've had some good times, and we'll have many more, but I hope you now know that it won't be all pleasant, even for you."

All I know is that my life has changed. Before, I was just

a stray. Now I am a follower of my Master, and that is good news.

19

"Do You Want to See?"

Another day, we are at the Temple. Jesus is teaching the people. His disciples are busy with small groups, relating the miraculous things they have seen Jesus do. I am, as usual, playing with the kids.

All of a sudden we hear an uproar in the distance. We all stop what we're doing. The mothers hustle their children away. Jesus calls me over and says, "Pup, stay close—this could get ugly."

I see a large crowd of angry men come up to Jesus, a couple of them dragging with them a woman. The other men are all carrying big stones.

I notice something strange about the woman—a lot of her clothing has been ripped off. She's trying to keep her body covered by holding the rags to it.

The man who seems to be in charge says to Jesus, "Teacher, this woman was caught in the very act of committing adultery."

The woman is holding her head down, not looking at anyone. Her face, what I can see of it, is red with embarrassment.

Jesus is very careful not to look at her. I think he doesn't want to add to her pain. He does seem to be angry, but not at her. I think he's mad at those who have brought her to him.

The man continues, "In our law Moses commanded that such a woman be stoned to death. What is your opinion?"

Jesus, without saying one word, bends over and starts doodling in the dust with his finger.

They ask him again, but again he does not answer. He just goes on doodling.

They become more and more irritated, and finally the one who has been speaking for the crowd shouts, "I *said*, WHAT IS YOUR OPINION?"

Jesus straightens up, looks him in the eye, and then very forcefully says to them all, "Let the one among you who is sinless be the first to throw a stone at her." And then he bends down and continues his doodling.

A look of understanding comes upon them, one by one. And as it does, they drop their stones and slowly slink away.

The first to leave are the older ones. I still don't recognize anything that Jesus is doodling, and no one else is getting close enough to see. But Jesus' followers start snickering as the men leave one by one. *All* of those men leave.

When they are gone, Jesus straightens up, and says to the woman, "Is there no one left to condemn you?"

Still embarrassed, she says quietly, "No one, sir."

"Well," Jesus says, "neither do I condemn you. Be on your way. But don't sin anymore."

The look on her face changes. The shame and embarrassment are gone; she is at peace. She says, "Thank you. Praise God."

As she leaves, all the onlookers also praise God. And they compliment Jesus on his wise handling of a very dangerous situation.

A little later, when it is time for us to move on, Jesus says to me, "Pup, that woman now has a whole new life because she chose to be open to the power of God. But I don't think many of those men were changed. I'm afraid they will ignore the gift they were just offered."

On the next day, the Sabbath, we continue our journey, and along the way we come across a beggar who obviously has been blind from birth. Thomas asks Jesus, "Teacher, who committed the sin that is the reason he was born blind? He himself, or one of his parents?"

Jesus smiles and says, "It's not because of anyone's sin. This man was born blind so that in him God could show what he can do."

Jesus goes over to the man and asks him, "Do you want to see?"

He says, "Oh, yes!"

Jesus bends down and spits on the dust. Out of this moistened dust he makes a paste, which he rubs on the man's eyes. Then he says, "Go wash your face in the Pool of Siloam."

As the man is leaving, Thomas says, "What was that all about?"

Jesus smiles and says, "You'll see later. We haven't seen the last of him. And this will be a hard lesson for the Pharisees."

Some time later, the man comes walking toward us, and he is not walking as a blind man would.

He can see. But he looks upset.

Jesus says, "What's wrong? Aren't you glad you can see?"

"Yes," he says, "but it's also causing me some trouble."

Jesus invites him to sit down and tell us all about it.

"Well," he says, as he sits down, "one day I was begging on the road, as usual, and this man came up to me. Later I was told that his name is Jesus."

I see just a hint of a smile on Jesus' face.

The man continues, "He asked me if I wanted to see! I could hardly believe my ears. All my life I had wanted this so much, but could hardly admit it even to myself, because it seemed impossible. But I did admit it to him; I told him yes.

"Well, then I heard him spit, and then he rubbed something on my eyes, and then he told me to go wash up in the Pool of Siloam. And when I washed the stuff off my eyes, I could see."

Jesus says, "Well, this is good. How is it causing you problems?"

The man shakes his head and says, "Some of my neighbors saw me and started arguing about whether or not it was really me. When I assured them that it was, they asked how this happened, and I told them about Jesus."

"So then what happened?" asks the Zealot.

"They took me to the Pharisees," he says. "And then it got really bad."

"Why?" asks Matthew.

"Well, they had me tell the story again. And after hearing it, some of them told me, 'That man cannot be from God, since he breaks the Sabbath laws.' But others asked, 'How could a sinner perform such miracles?' And finally they all asked me point-blank, 'Who do you say he is?' And I answered, 'He is a prophet.'"

"Well done," Jesus says.

"Then they brought in my parents, to interrogate them. I could see the fear on their faces. I felt sorry for them. When they were questioned, they said, 'We know that our son was born blind. But we do not know how it is that he can now see. Ask him—he's old enough to answer for himself!' So then the Pharisees said to me, 'Under oath, tell the truth! We know that this man who cured you is a sinner!' And I said to them, 'I don't know whether or not he is a sinner. All I know is that I was blind before, and now I can see.'"

Jesus asks, "And did they accept your response?"

"No," he says, "they accused me of being a follower of Jesus. They called *me* a sinner—and expelled me from the synagogue!"

With great kindness, Jesus looks at him and says, "Do you believe in the Son of Man?"

The man answers, "Tell me who he is, sir, so that I can believe in him."

Jesus says, "You have already seen him. He is the one talking with you now."

The man exclaims, "I believe, Lord!" and falls on his knees.

Then Jesus says, "I came into this world for judgment, such that those who do not see might see, and those who do see might be blinded."

At this, some of the Pharisee spies that are always with us exclaim, "Surely you're not saying that we are blind, are you?"

Jesus answers, "If you were, then you would not be guilty. But since you say, 'We can see,' your guilt remains."

Then Jesus says to the man who used to be blind, "Why don't you stay with us for a few days, and witness a deeper truth than your eyes can reveal?"

The man joyfully agrees to stay with us for a while. And this makes our spies even more upset; some of them quickly leave.

As we continue on, Jesus picks me up, and, rubbing my ear, he says, "Pup, those who left are going to report to their leaders. But they're not going to tell the truth of what they have seen and heard. Instead, they will tell the leaders what they want to hear."

When he puts me down, he says, "Greater wonders await us, Pup. But the greater the miracles, the more unsettled the spiritually blind will become."

I think to myself, I have seen so much that I don't think

anything will surprise me. And besides, what is really great about my Master is the love that he offers.

20

"I Am the Resurrection, and the Life"

At the end of one of his teaching days, some people rush up to Jesus and say, "We have been sent by Martha and Mary to find you and tell you that your friend Lazarus is very sick. They ask that you come to him at once."

Jesus says, "Thank you, but tell them not to worry. The end result of his illness will not be death. Rather, this illness will bring glory to God, and in such a way that by means of it the Son of God will be glorified."

After that, we keep working with the people of that area for two more days.

On the night of the second day, as everyone else is going to sleep, Jesus and I go off to pray, as we so often do. He picks me up and holds me, and says, "Pup, Martha and Mary's faith in me is being tested. I know they will pass the test, but tonight they are crying their eyes out."

I think of that first time that I was at their house—that time when Mary spent all her time petting me and listening to Jesus, and Martha got upset because of all the work she felt forced to do all by herself. I look up at Jesus, to ask him why they are now crying, and he says, "Pup, they have buried Lazarus."

I am shocked. Not just by what Jesus has told me, but also by the fact that we did not go to Lazarus right after the messengers came. When we get to bed, I toss and turn all night.

The next morning, Jesus calls everyone together and says, "Today we will go back to Judea."

"But Jesus," says Philip, "just the other day the people there were wanting to stone you. Are you sure you want to go back there now?"

"Our friend Lazarus is asleep," says Jesus. "I need to go wake him up."

Judas says, "If he's able to sleep, he'll recover. Why bother going there now?"

Jesus then says, "Let me speak plainly. Lazarus is dead. And for your sakes I'm glad I wasn't there. This way you can come to believe in the power of the good news. Let's go."

Thomas says to the other apostles, "Let's go so that we can die with him."

As we are walking, Jesus picks me up and holds me, and I see tears in his eyes. "Pup," he says, "I wish that my friends did not have to go through all this sorrow, but the joy that is coming will completely wipe it from their memories. And what I do in Bethany will not be forgotten by anyone there. Didn't I tell you greater things were at hand?"

By the time we arrive, Bethany is crowded. Many friends of the family have come in from Jerusalem to comfort Martha and Mary. Now a message is sent to the house, telling them that Jesus has finally come.

Martha comes out to meet him, and says, "If you had been here, my brother would not have died! But I know that even now God will give you whatever you ask him for."

Jesus says, "Your brother will live again."

She replies, "I know that he will come back to life at the resurrection on the last day."

Jesus says, in a tone of authority, "I *am* the resurrection, and the life. Whoever believes in me will, even if they die, yet live, and whoever lives and believes in me will never die. Do you believe this?"

In a firm voice she says, "Yes, Lord; I believe that you are the Messiah, the Son of God, the one who was to come into the world."

Just then her sister Mary comes out, along with many of the mourners.

Mary comes up to Jesus and falls at his feet, saying the same thing Martha said: "If you had been here, my brother would not have died!" She and all her friends are crying.

In a sad voice, Jesus says, "Where have you buried him?"

Martha answers, "Come see."

When Jesus gets to the tomb, he cries too. The tomb is a cave with a huge stone moved to the front of it. I hear many of the people say, "See how much he loved him?" But others are saying, "He gave sight to that blind man, didn't he? So, why couldn't he have kept Lazarus from dying?"

When I hear this criticism, I start to growl. But Jesus looks at me and says, "Pup, I have another way of silencing our critics."

Then, in a loud voice, he says, "Take the stone away!"

Martha touches his arm and says, "But Jesus, by now there will be an awful stench; he's been dead for four days."

Very gently and lovingly, he looks into her eyes and says, "Didn't I tell you that you would see God's glory if you believed?"

She lets go of him, and he moves forward. He looks up to heaven, as I have so often seen him do when we pray at night.

Then, in a strong voice, he says, "Thank you, Father, for listening to me."

Then, so quietly that only those of us who are close to him can hear, he says, "I know that you always listen to me, but I am saying this for the benefit of the people here, so that they may believe that you sent me."

And then, in a voice full of power and authority, he calls out, "Lazarus, come out!"

At first it seems that nothing is happening. We all stay very quiet, holding our breath.

All of a sudden we see movement in the cave. And then what looks like just a huge bundle of linen comes wobbling to the mouth of the cave. Jesus says to the ones who rolled the stone away, "Unbind him, and let him go."

Some of the people cry out in joy. Some cannot, because they are in shock.

I turn around, and see some of the Pharisee spies slip off from the crowd. I bark to call attention to them. Jesus looks at me and says, "I wonder what they will say about this, Pup. I wonder how they will twist it to their own advantage."

Many of the people who were not up close to the tomb ask others what happened. Some of them even ask the ones who rolled back the stone if this whole thing was a hoax. They think that maybe Lazarus wasn't really dead. But those who rolled the stone back keep saying, "No, we buried him. This is our job; we know death, and the smell it gives off. We smelled it when we buried him. And it was overwhelming when we rolled the stone back. But as soon as Jesus called him to come out, the smell disappeared. When we saw him hobble out into the sunlight, we ourselves nearly died, of fright. But when we unwrapped him, there was no sign of rotting flesh. In fact, his skin looked as healthy as a baby's."

It takes a long time for the crowd to break up.

When all those people are finally gone, Jesus asks Martha, "Would you let us stay at your house tonight?"

"With great pleasure," she says quietly. "Whatever we have is yours."

With a twinkle in his eye, Jesus says, "That last time,

you were too busy making lunch to let us enjoy your company. When we left, you said you wouldn't make that mistake again."

Martha smiles and says, "With all the food that the mourners brought, there's nothing for me to do except be with you, my friend."

Jesus just smiles and says, "Good!"

That night, everyone stays up very late. By the time Jesus and I get a chance to go for our nighttime prayer, I am very tired. Jesus picks me up and carries me, saying, "Yes, Pup, it has been a busy day. I'm tired too. Today many people have seen the power of the good news. Some are attracted to it, and will be among our best supporters. But others fear it, and are hostile to us. I know that even now they are plotting to put an end to me. But no matter what they do to me, I want you to know that, just as Lazarus was raised from the dead, I will rise again."

Tonight Jesus stays up a long time praying. He holds me the whole time. I even fall asleep in his arms. As I drop off to sleep, I think how lucky I am to have the love of my Master. A love that really does give life.

21

"Love One Another as I Have Loved You"

Just before sunrise, Jesus and I go off for our morning prayer. I always like these special times; I feel like God is right here with us. But this morning there is something different. In Jesus' prayer I sense an extra intensity that makes me a little nervous.

After this prayer time we usually go right back to the disciples, but not today. Jesus says, "Come here, Pup. I need to talk to you."

Now I am more than a little nervous. Did I do something wrong?

Jesus says reassuringly, "Don't be afraid, Pup. It's nothing you've done. I just want you to know what is about to happen, so that you're prepared."

I climb up on his lap, and he starts petting me, and says, "We have been together for a long time, Pup. We have had some really good times, and some tough times. But we are going to be entering into a stage of life that will have both the darkest, most painful times we could imagine, and the brightest, happiest experiences we could ever dream of."

I lick his face, wondering what he is talking about.

"Pup," he continues, "I know how much you love me, and you know I love you."

I wag my tail. He has become more than my Master; he is my best friend.

He lifts me up, looks into my eyes, and says very seriously, "You are going to see things done to me that will break your heart. Just remember that everything is happening for a reason. And you must have faith in me—faith that in the end not only will everything work out, but you will have a joy beyond anything you can imagine." He holds me tight, and I feel his love. Then he gets up, puts me down, and says, "Let's go, Pup. It is time to begin the final victory of the good news."

In our group are not only the apostles, but also some of the women whose lives have been touched by Jesus. When we get back to the camp, Jesus calls over Peter and John and says to them, "Today is the day we'll be having our Passover supper. Take Mom, Mary Magdalene, Joanna, and Susanna with you, and go into town and find a place for us."

Peter says, "Where are we going to find a place at this late date?"

Jesus says, "When you get into the city, you will see a man carrying a jar of water. Follow him into the house that he enters, and say to the master of the house, 'The Teacher says, "My time has come. Where is the room where my disciples and I will eat the Passover meal?"' He will take you upstairs and show you a large room that is all prepared. There the women will prepare the meal for us."

Peter gets the small group together, and off they go to the city. The rest of us break camp and get ready to join them. Everyone is in a good mood, because it is the time of the Passover. But when I look at Jesus, he seems also to have other things on his mind.

Some time later, Peter and John return, and Peter tells Jesus, "Everything happened just as you said it would. The room is a big one. Your mother is supervising and helping in all the preparations. We tried to help, but were asked to leave so that we wouldn't get in the way!"

I can easily imagine how much love Mary and the others are putting into everything.

John says, "They're having a great time preparing the feast. They work together as if they'd been friends all their lives. I have a feeling this will be a Passover we will never forget."

Jesus smiles and says, "*That* I am sure of!"

Then he calls everyone together and says, "It's time to leave. Peter and John will show us where we'll be celebrating Passover tonight."

▲▼▲▼▲

As we walk up the stairs to that room, I notice a couple of things. First of all, the smell is great. My mouth starts watering. But even more surprising is the sound of the women working. They are laughing and having a grand time.

When we come in, Mary says, "You're here already? We're not quite ready for you."

Jesus walks over, gives her a hug, and says, "Actually, that's good, because I need some time with the Twelve before we sit down to eat. We'll go to the other part of the room and stay out of your way."

Jesus motions all of us over and tells the apostles, "Everyone sit down in a circle. I have to get something from the kitchen; I'll be right back."

Jesus and I go into the kitchen. I am wondering what he is going to do.

"Pup," he says, "it is time to show my disciples what it means to be a follower of mine." Then he gets a basin, a pitcher that he puts water in, and some towels. As he walks out of the kitchen, he calls back to me, "Come on, Pup, stay out of the women's way. Come help me wash some feet."

When we join the apostles, Jesus says to them, "Please take off your sandals."

They do this, looking at one another, wondering what is happening. Jesus, meanwhile, puts on an apron.

He goes up to Thaddaeus, kneels down, pours water over his feet, washes them, dries them with a towel, and then tells him he can put his sandals back on. He does this same thing with one apostle after the other. As he is doing this, they are looking at him like he has lost his mind.

Finally Jesus comes to Peter, and kneels down in front of him. I notice that Peter has his sandals back on, so I bite the strap of one of them and pull on it. Peter looks at me and says, "Get away from me, Pup." But he says it in a good-natured way; I know he's not mad at me.

Peter says, "Lord, *you're* going to wash *my* feet?"

Jesus says, "You don't understand now what I'm doing, but later you will."

Peter says, "Washing feet is something to be done by a servant, not by you, the Teacher. At no time—not now, not ever—will you wash my feet!"

Jesus smiles and shakes his head, and says, "Oh, Peter! Unless I wash you, you will have no share in my life."

Peter, looking shocked, says loudly, "Then, Lord, wash not just my feet, but also my hands and my head!"

Jesus is now laughing. "Typical Peter!" he says. "Listen. Anyone who has taken a bath is clean all over, and doesn't need anything washed, except for the feet. You are now clean, inside and out—all but one of you."

As he adds that last part, he glances at Judas, who looks away.

After washing Peter's feet, Jesus takes off the apron and sits down with the apostles, and says, "Do you understand what I have just done for you? You call me 'Teacher' and 'Lord,' and rightly so, for so I am. If, therefore, I, the Lord and Teacher, have washed your feet, you ought to wash one another's feet."

Thomas says, "You literally want us to wash each other's feet?"

"That's not what he's saying," answers Philip. "Can't you see that Jesus is telling us that we need to be the servants of others, just as he has been a servant to us? We should not think that anything is beneath our dignity to do, in the name of God and the good news—isn't that what you're telling us, Jesus?"

Jesus smiles at Philip and says, "Well done. Yes, that's exactly what I was trying to teach you all."

I jump up on Philip's leg, wagging my tail. Philip gives me a big smile and says, "It was nothing, Pup. Any one of us could have figured out what the Master was saying. All we have to do is listen carefully."

Jesus says, "And listen carefully is what I want you all

to do. I have a few more things I want to tell you before we eat."

Jesus pauses. I can see on his face that what he is about to say is something painful.

He says, "The glory of God is about to be revealed in the Son of Man. I am the one in whom the glory will be seen. I will not be with you for much longer. And where I am going, you cannot now follow me, though later you will."

John groans, and then whispers, "No."

Matthew exclaims, "It can't be!"

James says, "We'll be lost without you."

Peter, the last to speak, says, "Lord, why can't I follow you now? I am ready to go to prison or even die for you!"

Jesus looks at each of them in turn, and then says, "All of you will run away, as sheep do when their shepherd is killed."

Peter protests, "Even if the rest leave you, I never will!"

Jesus says emphatically, "I tell you, Peter, that before the rooster crows, you will three times have claimed not to even know me."

Peter very indignantly says, "That will never happen!" And all the others nod in agreement.

Jesus looks at me with knowing eyes. I can see that what he has just predicted will come true. I am sad and climb up on his leg, and he looks down and says to me, "Don't forget what I told you this morning." I am starting to understand that this is going to be one of those dark days he told me about.

Then he says to them, "I don't want you to be distracted from what I am about to tell you. So put all that other stuff out of your minds, and listen carefully."

He waits until he has everyone's attention, and then says, "I want to make very clear what the good news that we have been spreading is all about. What I have done is give you a new commandment: Love one another. It's new in that I mean you must love one another *as I have loved you.* This is how everyone will know that you are my disciples—by this love that you have for one another."

Matthew says, "Jesus, we have been together so long. You know that we care for each other and won't let anything come between us."

Jesus says, "I know you have become a family. But sometimes in a family there are jealousies and hurt feelings."

When he says "jealousies," he looks at John and James, whose mother caused something of a problem when she asked that they be the ones to sit at his right and left in the Kingdom.

He continues, "Make sure that such feelings never divide the family of love which I have put together. Also, all those who choose to accept the good news when you preach it to them must understand that they are bound by this same new commandment to love one another."

Thomas says, "But we can't go on without you. We'll be like lost little children."

"Don't let your hearts be troubled or afraid," says Jesus. "I am going to my Father's house, to prepare a place for you, and when I have done that, I will come back and take you to myself, so that where I am you also can be. You know the way to where I am going."

"Lord," says Thomas, "we don't know where you are going. So, how can we know the way?"

Jesus says, "I am the way, and the truth and the life. No one comes to the Father except through me. If you had known me, then you would have known my Father also. From this point on you do know him and have seen him."

Philip says, "Lord, show us the Father; that will be enough for us."

Jesus says, "I've been with you all this time, Philip, and you still don't know who I am?"

Philip looks puzzled.

Jesus, looking disappointed, says, "Do you not believe that I am in the Father and the Father is in me? The words I speak to you I do not speak on my own. They come from the Father. *Believe* me when I say that I am in the Father and the Father is in me. If for no other reason, believe it because of the things you have seen me do. I am telling you the truth: whoever believes in me will do the works I do—in fact, even greater works than these— because I am going to the Father. And whatever you ask in my name, I will do, so that the Father will be glorified in the Son."

Here Jesus pauses. The apostles stay very quiet. Jesus seems lost in thought, so I jump up on his lap, trying to let him know he is not alone.

He holds me, and rubs my ear, as they all think over what he has just said. He bends down and whispers, "PupPup, they are beginning to realize just how important the good news is, and the responsibility they have accepted by embracing it."

Thaddaeus, looking a little confused, says, "Lord, this is too much for us to take in. How are we ever going to remember everything you have told us and taught us?"

Jesus says, "I have told you all these things while I am still with you. But the Helper, the Holy Spirit, whom the Father will send in my name, he will teach you everything and remind you of all that I have said to you."

The apostles are again deep in thought. Jesus hugs me tight and whispers, "Pup, I know this is a lot for them to take in right now, but my time is short. I have to make sure that everything my Father has asked me to share with them has been covered."

When he says that his time is short, I whimper. I do not want to hear that my Master has to leave us all.

He pets me and whispers, "I know that what is going to happen will be hard on all of them. But I feel it will be the hardest on Mom and you. Don't forget what I said to you this morning."

This time it is James Junior that breaks the silence. He says, "Jesus, what can we expect as we continue your work of spreading the good news?"

"James, and all of you," Jesus says, "I don't think you will like what I have to tell you. You will be expelled from the synagogues, and the time will even come when people will think that by killing you they are serving God. But when the world hates you, just remember that it hated me first. If you belonged to the world, then the world would love you; it loves its own. But I have chosen you out of the world, and you do not belong to it; and so the world will hate you. Remember what I told you: The servant is not greater than the master. If they persecuted me, they will persecute you too. They will do this to you on my account, because they do not know the One who sent me.

"Since I am sending you, I have told you this so that when the time comes that they do these things, you will remember it. The Holy Spirit will help you do that, and will give you the guidance you will need."

Jesus is still lovingly holding me, but I feel as if he is holding all of us. It is very quiet. Everyone is again deep in thought.

Then we hear Mary call out, "All right, we're ready now. I hope we didn't keep you waiting too long."

Jesus smiles at her, puts me down, goes and gives her a big hug, and says, "No, as a matter of fact, it's as if you knew the perfect time to come get us. I just finished saying to everyone what I needed to say."

Jesus turns to the apostles and says, "It's time to celebrate the Passover." And then he turns to me and says, "Come on, Pup, we'll find a place for you."

They all sit at the table, with Jesus in the middle, and I sit beside him. The women sit close to the kitchen, so that they can easily bring in the food.

After everyone is seated, Jesus says, "I have really looked forward to sharing this meal with you before I suffer. For I tell you, I will not be eating the Passover supper again until it is fulfilled in the kingdom of God."

Then, looking over at the women, he says, "I want to thank in a special way you women, not only for preparing the meal, but for all of your active involvement in the sharing of the good news."

And then, looking down at me, he adds, "And you, Pup, for walking this long road with me, from the beginning. For giving me joy, comfort, and love." I wag my tail, in thanks for the compliment I've just been given by my Master.

Then Jesus asks us all to stand, and says, "Friends, let us begin this celebration with prayer. Notice that I am calling you friends, not servants. Servants do not know what their master is doing. I call you friends because I have told you everything I heard from my Father. You did not choose me; I chose you, and commissioned you to go and bear fruit—fruit that will last. The greatest love one can have is to give one's life for a friend. Remember, you are my friends, and always will be if you do what I command you to do, which is to love one another."

Then, looking up to heaven, he says, "Father, the hour has come. Give glory to your Son, so that your Son may give glory to you. I have made you known to these you have given me out of the world. They have obeyed your word, and now they know that everything you gave me is from you. I gave them the good news that you entrusted to me, and they received it. They know that it is true, and that you have sent it through me to them, and that they are to bring it to the whole world. I now pray for them.

"Father, keep them safe by the power of this name of yours that you have given me, so that they may be one just as we are. The world will hate them. I do not ask that you take them out of the world, but I do ask that you keep them safe from the Evil One.

"I pray not only for them, but also for all those who will believe in me because of their spreading of the good news.

"Father, you know that all those who embrace the good news are my friends. I ask that you take care of these friends of your Son . . ."

When Jesus finishes this prayer, he asks everyone to sit down.

Then he asks everyone to pay very close attention to what he is about to do. He says, "I have one more very important thing to share with you."

He takes a loaf of bread that was sitting in front of him, and he blesses it, and breaks it, and then holds it out to the apostles, saying, "Take and eat: this is my body."

He then hands it to Peter. Peter carefully accepts it, breaks off a piece, and hands the rest on to the others.

When Peter has eaten his portion, I seem to sense a change in him. He seems to be more on Jesus' wavelength. And as the other apostles each take and eat this bread which Jesus has said is his body, I seem to sense the same change in them.

Then Jesus takes a cup of wine, gives thanks, and holds out the cup to the apostles, saying, "Drink from this, all of you, for this is my blood, the blood of the new covenant;

blood to be shed for you and for all, for the forgiveness of sins."

Once again, Peter is the first to receive what Jesus offers. And after he drinks from the cup, he hands it to the other apostles to drink in their turn.

After they have all received the cup, Jesus says, "Do this as my memorial. I tell you, I will not be drinking wine with you again until the day I drink the new wine with you, in the kingdom of God."

With a look of accomplishment on his face, he then sits down with the others and says, "Now we can finish this Passover meal."

As the traditional Passover food is brought in, John leans over to Jesus and says, "That was beautiful, but what you said is frightening. You're giving us an awful lot of responsibility."

"John," Jesus says, "I know that most of you will live up to my expectations."

John asks, "What do you mean most of us?"

Jesus says, "I know that I will be betrayed by someone sitting at this table."

For a moment it gets very quiet, and then they all start asking one another who that could be. But, from my place next to Jesus, I catch the smell of fear coming from one of them.

I get up and growl. I will protect my Master.

Jesus looks down at me and says, "Pup, I told you, everything is going to happen for a reason. I appreciate your desire to protect me, but you have to let things take their proper course. Do sit down."

I am very tempted to disobey my Master. But I have to believe he knows what he is doing.

John leans over and whispers to Jesus, "Which one of us is it?"

Jesus whispers back, "It's the one I will give a piece of bread to, after dipping it in the dish."

Just then more loaves of bread are brought out and set around the table.

Jesus breaks off a piece, dips it into the closest sauce dish, and, with a look full of love and sadness, hands it to Judas.

Their eyes meet, and Judas says, "Surely, Teacher, it's not me, is it?"

And Jesus answers quietly, "You said it."

Well, John may be surprised, but I'm sure not. Judas is the one who had the smell of fear coming from him when Jesus was talking about being betrayed.

And now there is an even worse smell. It's the devil, actually getting into Judas.

Jesus says to Judas, "What you are going to do, do quickly."

Judas gets up and leaves.

The other apostles, not having heard what Jesus said to John, ask, "Why did Judas leave?"

Jesus just says, "He has something to do."

We then go on with our meal. The food that the women prepared is excellent, and Jesus makes sure I get my share. Everyone seems to be in a good mood, although I sense in Jesus some anxiousness.

Eventually the meal comes to an end. Jesus goes to find his mother, and he gives her a long hug. His eyes are shiny as he says, "You stay here with the other women and help them clean up if you want. And then take them home with you—I don't want you to be alone."

She asks, "Son, are you all right? Will you be coming home tonight?"

He hugs her again and whispers to her, "Both questions, no. And before going anywhere else, I need to go off and pray for strength. I will take Pup and the eleven apostles that are still with me."

Mary now has tears in her eyes. She seems to know by motherly instinct that her son is keeping something from her to protect her. They hug again, and then Jesus turns to the apostles and says, "Would you all come with me tonight? I need your support."

They nod, and walk down the stairs with him. Mary calls me over and gives me a hug, and says, "Pup, take good care of Jesus. Don't let him out of your sight. I am sure that he is going to need your love. I think something is about to happen that he's not telling me."

As I run after the group and catch up to Jesus, I know that she is right. I am glad that I cannot talk. I've heard Jesus' prayers at night and I know about the dark times coming. And yes, I will stay close to my Master.

22

"Your Will Be Done"

As we are leaving the house, Bartholomew asks Jesus where we are going.

Jesus, looking very serious, says, "I need to pray for the strength to make it through the next test. And I want you all to pray with me."

Because of what Jesus told me at our morning prayer, I feel very uneasy. I don't run ahead, as I usually do, but instead I walk right next to him, with my head down.

John notices the way I'm acting, and he says to Jesus, "Looks like something's wrong with PupPup. Think it could be indigestion? Our little friend maybe ate too much of the Passover food?"

"No," Jesus says, "I think Pup is sensing something, and is upset by it."

I'm a little angry; what's wrong with these apostles? Can't they see that Jesus is even more upset than I am? They're supposed to be his friends, and yet they can't even see how much he is suffering.

Finally we get to a place called Gethsemane. This is a garden that we've been to quite often, to pray and to have some time away from the crowds. All of Jesus' helpers know about it.

Jesus tells the apostles, "I'm going further into the garden. I want you to stay here and pray—pray hard that you not be put to the test."

Then he asks Peter, James, and John to come with him. And then he looks down at me and says, "Pup, you are always with me in prayer; be with me tonight."

As we move deeper into the garden, Peter says, "Jesus, I'm glad you have invited me to be with you in your prayer. As I told you at the Passover meal, I will never leave you."

Jesus looks at him and says, "Peter, I want you to remember what I told you."

Peter looks upset that Jesus still thinks he will desert him.

Jesus then says to him and James and John, "You three, pray together here. Pray for yourselves and for the others, that you will not be put to the test. Pup and I will go a little farther, to be alone with God."

The three of them sit down and start praying. Jesus and I move a little distance away, fifty steps or so.

Jesus kneels, with me at his side, and then, looking up to heaven and stretching out his arms, he says, "Father, you know I want only to do your will. Please, if this is possible, let this cup of suffering pass me by. But let be as you would have it, not as I would."

After a while we go back to Peter, James, and John, and find that they have fallen asleep! Jesus says, "PupPup, look at them—they can't even stay awake with me for this short time. I wonder how they will survive what will be happening in the next couple of days. Pup, wake up Peter!"

I run over to Peter. I am so mad at him—how can he sleep when Jesus is in so much pain? So I jump right on top of him, not trying at all to be gentle. But Jesus looks at me and says, "Not in anger, Pup."

Peter yells, "Pup! What do you think you're doing?" And this wakes up the other two, who look around sheepishly, but say nothing.

Peter is about to open his mouth again, but then he sees Jesus standing there. Jesus says, "Peter, how is it that you were not able to keep vigil with me for even one hour? Pray that you will not be put to the test. The spirit is willing, but the flesh is weak."

As we go back to our place of prayer, Jesus says, as if thinking out loud, "I know that all of the terrible pain that I am being asked to suffer is for the redemption of all people. It will free them of the debt caused by their sins."

This time he kneels sitting back on his feet, with his head down and his hands in his lap. He looks very much like a child. I sit next to him, my head also bowed. In a quiet voice he says, "Father, for you all things are possible. So I am asking that you not make your Son drink this cup of suffering. Please, please spare me this. Just the prospect of it is killing me. But what I want more than anything else is to do your will. I want terribly to be spared this, but only if that is what *you* want."

After quite some time, Jesus gets up and we go back to Peter, James, and John. And again, all three are asleep. We go past them and find that the apostles near the garden entrance are also asleep. Jesus says with a sigh, "Pup, it is disappointing, isn't it? But they're tired out, not just from today but from all this time that we've been on the road, preaching the good news. Well, Pup, wake them all up."

I start barking as if we are being attacked. The apostles jump up in alarm. Peter draws his sword; but when he sees Jesus, his face turns red with embarrassment. They all look down, realizing that they have again let Jesus down; none of them has anything to say.

Jesus just begs them, "Please be with me in prayer. You need to pray tonight like you've never prayed before."

Then Jesus and I go off to our place of prayer a third time, while the apostles get back into their two groups and start praying.

This time Jesus throws himself to the ground, and he is crying. I lie down right next to him. He says pleadingly, "Father, what I see coming will be horrible to endure. If you are willing to, *please* take this cup away from me. Yet if you do not see fit to take it away without my drinking it, your will be done!"

While he is still face down on the ground, I sense something happening. I get up, and I see one of the angels who appeared to us after the temptations in the desert. I nudge Jesus with my nose, and he looks up and recognizes the angel.

The angel comes over to him and gives him the strength to pray so hard that he sweats big drops of blood. And then he stands up, gives a big sigh, and, looking and sounding like he is at peace, says, "Father, your will be done. I will do all that you ask of me, and I will do it with love. Thank you for answering my prayer and sending your messenger to give me the strength I was needing."

Then he looks at me and says, "Let's go, Pup. In a few minutes I will have to be without even you. My Father has asked me to walk the last part of this road alone. In that way I will show everyone that living the good-news life does involve times when you have to stand up all alone for what is right."

Then he says, "Pup, let's go back and get the disciples. It is time for the Son of God to be handed over to the power of the Evil One."

We go over to where the disciples are—and once again we find them asleep. Jesus says, "Still sleeping? Still taking it easy?"

As soon as they hear this, they jump up again.

Then he says, "Get up; let's go. Look! My betrayer is coming, and he's bringing with him others trapped in the power of the Evil One."

As we start walking toward the garden gate, we are confronted by a large number of people—Pharisees, priests, teachers, elders, and the Temple Guard, along with many others. There must be close to a hundred altogether. They are carrying torches, swords, and clubs, and are being guided by Judas.

I plant myself in front of Jesus and growl and show my teeth. I will not let anything happen to my Master.

Jesus looks at me and says, "Pup, you must have trust that what I told you is the way it has to be. Remember, God sent an angel to strengthen me. Stand off to the side so that you don't get hurt."

Jesus calls out, "Who are you looking for?"

They shout back, "Jesus of Nazareth! Which one is he?"

Jesus says, "I am."

As if these words have punched them, they all move back, so quickly that they fall. Then they get up and move toward Jesus again.

In a tone of authority, Jesus says again, "Who are you looking for?"

Again they answer, "Jesus of Nazareth!"

Jesus, in that same tone of authority, says, "I told you already, I am the one you are looking for."

As Jesus is speaking, Peter draws his sword and strikes at the nearest man in the mob, and cuts off part of his right ear. The man turns out to be a servant of the high priest.

Jesus says to Peter, "Put your sword back into its sheath. All who take the sword will perish by the sword. Don't you know that I could call on my Father for help and he would immediately send me more than twelve armies of angels? But then the scriptures would not be fulfilled."

Jesus then takes the servant by the head and, just by touching the ear, heals him, saying, "I know it is not your choice to be here. There is no reason for you to suffer."

Some of the people look extremely impressed, but they do not say anything, for fear of their leaders.

Judas comes forward, stands in front of Jesus, and starts to put his arms around him.

Jesus says quietly, "Judas, are you betraying the Son of Man with a kiss?"

Judas does not answer, but does kiss Jesus on the cheek. And immediately members of the Temple Guard run up and grab Jesus.

Jesus says to them, "Did you have to come with swords and clubs to capture me, as if I were an outlaw? Day after day I sat down and taught in the Temple. If you wanted to arrest me, why didn't you do it there?"

Giving Jesus no response, the leader of the Temple Guard asks one of the chief priests, "And what should we do with his followers?" By this time quite a few of his followers are here.

The chief priest says, "Take them too."

But Jesus says, "It's me that you want, so let these others go free."

When the disciples hear this, they all start running, every which way. One of the guards goes after a boy who was hiding among the trees, and grabs him by his robe; but he slips out of it and runs away naked.

Jesus turns to me and yells, "Pup, go to Mom!"

I don't budge. I will not leave my Master.

Jesus, looking sad, says, "Pup, I am your Master. I am telling you—go to Mom, *now*!"

What can I do? I have to obey. I run, and keep from getting caught by the guards.

But I do dive under a bush and look back, and I see them tie Jesus up and start leading him away. They are pushing and shoving him. It breaks my heart.

Then I remember that Jesus told me, "They will do things to me that will break your heart." My Master is right again. I wish that this time he hadn't been.

I run as fast as I can to the house where Mary is staying. And all I can think about is how alone my Master is.

23

"You Will See the Son of Man"

When I get to the house, I bark and scratch at the door, and can't stop panting.

Mary opens the door, and says, "Pup! I told you to stay with Jesus!"

I whimper and pull at her sleeve, and finally she says, "He sent you to me, didn't he?"

I bark and run to the gate. I want her to come with me to Jesus.

She says, "All right, we will go to him soon, but first

we've got to get you some water and have you rest some."

She puts down a bowl of water, but I ignore it and pull at her dress—I want her to follow me.

She looks at me sadly and says gently but firmly, "Pup, you'll be no good to Jesus unless you have water and some rest. Jesus sent you to me, so I am telling you, take some water and rest a bit. That will give me time to get ready to go with you."

I know she's right, so I do lap up the water.

Very soon, Mary is ready. The women who helped her with the Passover meal ask her, "Do you want us to go with you?" But she says, "No, you must stay here in case any of Jesus' disciples come. If they do, make them comfortable and ask them to wait for my return." Then, looking down at me, she says, "Let's go, Pup, and find out what has happened to Jesus."

As I am leading her back to where I left Jesus, Mary sees coming from that direction a woman she knows, so she asks her, "Do you know where my son is?"

The woman says, "I am so sorry. Your son has been arrested."

Mary thanks her for her sympathy, and then asks, "Where have they taken him?"

The woman points to a big building and says, "The house of Caiaphas, the high priest."

Mary looks at me and says, "I know a shortcut, Pup; follow me."

When we get to the building, I see that the crowd has grown even larger than it was at the garden. And I notice that the high priest has gathered around him the chief priests, elders, teachers of the Law, and Pharisees. I hear someone say that he is forming a council. He also has with him many members of the Temple Guard.

Those people are all talking together. We look around, but can't see Jesus. Mary leans down and whispers to me, "Pup, see if you can find any of the disciples. Some may have followed him here. But be very careful—I think you are well known as Jesus' shadow."

I think to myself, I doubt if any of them came here, since they ran away so fast. But Jesus did send me to be with Mary, so I will obey and defend her, just as I did my Master.

As I move through the crowd, most people just ignore me, and I don't pay any attention to them either. But then, suddenly, I pick up the scent of someone I know.

I think to myself, Oh, it can't be. But sure enough, about ten feet in front of me, there he is—Peter. He's sitting by the fire, warming himself.

I start to go over there, but then I stop, because I see a servant girl walking up to him.

She kind of squints at him and then says, "You were with Jesus of Nazareth."

I hear Peter deny it! He says to her, "I don't know what you're talking about."

Then he gets up and quickly moves away from the fire. He walks over to the passageway.

I come up to him and touch him on the leg, and he looks down and whispers, "What are you doing here, Pup? I thought Jesus told you to go to Mary."

I grab the bottom of his robe to lead him to her, and he seems to understand. He asks, "Is Mary here?"

I bark, as quietly as I can, and again I pull at his robe.

"No," he whispers, "it's too dangerous for her to be seen with me. I think they may already know who I am."

Just then a man comes up and says, "Yes, you are one of Jesus' followers—why, you even have his dog!"

Peter snaps at him, "I swear to God, I don't know the

man! And I've never seen this dog. It's just some mutt hanging around, begging for food."

At that I growl. And Peter adds, "If I knew this dog, would it be growling at me?"

Peter then walks to the gate, and I move away from him, but still keep an eye on him.

Just as he gets to the gate, another man comes up to him and exclaims, "You're a Galilean! You *are* one of Jesus' followers!"

Peter shouts, "You are wrong! I have never even seen him!"

But the man does not back down. He shouts, "Your accent gives you away!"

Peter shouts, "I swear to God that I am telling the truth! I do not know the man!"

Just then we hear, loud and clear, the crow of a rooster. Peter looks at me. I know that he is remembering what Jesus told him.

Peter puts his hands over his face and runs away.

I am very disappointed in him, and he has really hurt my feelings, but I still want to try to comfort him. However, Mary is still here, and I feel that she is my main responsibility. So I go back to where she is sitting.

When I get there, Jesus is being brought out to stand before the council. They still have him tied up. I *so* much want to go to him. But he did say for me to stay with Mary.

The priests ask that any witnesses against Jesus now present their cases.

Some people do come forward, but they contradict one another. One of them claims that he is buddy-buddy with tax collectors, while another one claims that he is telling people not to pay their taxes. One of them says, "He does his supposed miracles by the power of demons," while another one says, "He claims to be the Son of God."

Then a couple of them say, "This man said, 'I will destroy this temple made by human hands, and within three days I will build one not made by human hands." But they don't get very far with that one either.

Then Caiaphas, the high priest, says to Jesus, "Have you no answer to the charges they are making against you?"

Jesus just stands there, saying nothing.

Caiaphas says, "In the name of the living God—I hereby put you under oath—tell us: Are you the Messiah, the Son of God?"

Jesus looks at Caiaphas for a few seconds, and then answers, "I am. And I tell you, you will see the Son of Man seated at the right hand of the Almighty and coming on the clouds of heaven."

Caiaphas faces the council, rips his robe, and yells, "Blasphemy! We have no more need of witnesses! You heard what he just said. What say you?"

The council answers, "We find him guilty. And he must die!"

I look at Mary, and she is crying. I crawl up and lean against her leg and try to make her feel better. She starts rubbing my ear, just as Jesus would.

The high priest tells the council, "We cannot put him to death ourselves. Only the Romans have the power to execute someone. Tomorrow morning we will take Jesus to Pilate."

Then the council guards start insulting Jesus. They even spit on him. I get off of Mary's leg. I need to go over to my Master and protect him. But Mary whispers, "Stay here, Pup. Jesus would not want you to sacrifice yourself."

She is right, so I hold still. But then they blindfold him and start slapping him and then saying to him, "Prophesy for us, Messiah! Tell us who hit you!" I can't take any more. I have just got to get over there.

NO LONGER A STRAY

This time Mary grabs me and holds me back. She is still crying, and with her voice breaking she says, "No, Pup, I need you with me. I know that to see this hurts you just as it does me. But if we try anything now, they won't let us come back tomorrow, when they take him to Pilate. Jesus is going to need to have some loved ones with him to support him when he is brought before the governor. We will just have to suffer in quiet tonight, just as Jesus is doing. Let's go home."

When we get back to the house where Mary is staying, those women who helped her with the Passover meal are still there. They see that she has been crying and ask what has happened to Jesus. She tearfully tells them everything.

They tell her that they will stay with her through the night.

"That is not necessary," she says, "although it is very kind of you to offer."

But they remind her that Jesus said to her, "Take the women home with you—I don't want you to be alone." And when she hears this, she gratefully accepts their offer.

Everyone gets ready for bed. But I don't think any of us will get much sleep tonight.

Mary certainly won't. As I lie next to her bed, I hear her sobbing. And I can't get to sleep either. I can't stop thinking about how alone my Master is.

Jesus has told us all that God is his Father. How could any parent ask a child of theirs to go through what Jesus is going through?

My only comfort is that Jesus told me that in the end I will have a greater joy than I could ever imagine. Both Jesus and his Father must know things the rest of us don't. And I have never been lied to by my Master.

24

"My Kingdom Is Not of This World"

Early the next morning, when we are getting ready to join Jesus at the governor's palace, there is a knock at the door. I am afraid that someone is coming to take Mary away too. So I run to the door, ready to defend her if I have to.

She opens the door, and at first I relax. It's John, saying, "Mary, can I come in?"

She opens the door wide and says, "Of course, John. Wherever I am, you're always welcome."

I go up to John, but I'm still angry with him, so I don't give him much of a welcome.

He looks at me and says, "I know, Pup. I ran away. I am so ashamed of myself, and of all the rest of us disciples. You were the only one to stay. I bet you stayed till Jesus told you to leave, didn't you?"

Mary puts her arm around him and says consolingly, "John, don't feel that way. You know that Jesus understands, and would not want you to feel guilty because fear overcame you."

John says, "You're probably right."

Then Mary says, "John, have you heard anything else about any of Jesus' friends?"

John sadly looks down, and says very quietly, "Yes. I just heard that Judas hanged himself."

Mary gasps, "No! Why would he do such a thing?"

"From what I am told," John says, "he had a meeting with the elders, and they told him that if he showed them where they could find Jesus without the crowd that is always with him, they would pay him thirty pieces of silver. He may not have thought it would come to this—he had seen Jesus get out of tough situations before. But in any event, when he found out that Jesus had been condemned by the council, he apparently realized the full extent of the evil he had done. He went back to the elders and told them, 'I have sinned; I betrayed an innocent man!' And they laughed at him and said, 'What do we care? That is your problem; we have what we want.' He threw the coins down, right there in the Temple, and left. And a little while ago Matthew found him hanging from a tree."

Mary says, "That is terrible! What a tragedy. I know that Jesus would not have wanted him to do that. He would have forgiven him, if he had truly repented."

John says, "Yes. I even remember that when Judas left the Passover meal, Jesus did not seem angry with him. And when we asked where he was going, Jesus just said, 'He has something to do.' "

Mary then says, "John, we women are going to the governor's palace, to be there for Jesus when he is brought before Pilate. Would you like to go with us?"

John says, "Yes! Thank you so much. This time I will not run away."

I decide that John has suffered enough for his lack of courage, so I jump up on his lap. John rubs my belly and says, "I guess this means you have forgiven me for not standing with Jesus!" I wag my tail and lick his face.

Mary says, "We'd better get moving, or we won't be able to get close enough to hear what is going on."

We leave together, but we walk in silence, just thinking about Jesus and how he has affected our lives. I can hardly believe how different my life has been since I was found by my Master.

We arrive at the palace just as the elders and chief priests are leading Jesus to it. Jesus is in chains. When he sees us he smiles, and then nods in gratitude for our being with him in his time of need. Mary is about to call out to him, but, with a very slight movement of his head, he says no. We catch on that he does not want the crowd to know who we are.

Jesus is taken into the palace, but the elders and chief priests refuse to go in. They say that it would make them unclean. So Pilate comes back out to meet with them.

Pilate looks at the elders and says, "What charge do you bring against this man?"

They answer, "Is there really any need to go through all that? Surely you know that if he were not a criminal, we would never be handing him over to *you*."

Pilate says, "Let me get this straight. You expect me to hand down a sentence without even having been presented with a charge, let alone having given a verdict? Roman law does not allow for that. If that's what you want, then I suggest that you cleaner-than-thou people take him yourselves and try him according to your own law."

They answer, "We have already done that. The problem is that we are not allowed to put anyone to death."

"Well," says Pilate, "I am certainly not going to do that on the basis of no charge. So, what charge do you bring against this man?"

And they reply, "That of inciting rebellion among our people, by telling them not to pay taxes to the emperor, and by claiming that he himself is a king—ours, the Messiah."

Pilate goes back into the palace, brings Jesus out, and asks him, "Are you the king of the Jews?"

Jesus replies, "Are you asking me this on your own, or is it because of what others have said about me?"

Pilate retorts, "Am I a Jew? Your own nation, your chief priests, handed you over to me. What have you done?"

Jesus says, "My kingdom does not belong to this world. If it did, my followers would have fought to keep me from being handed over to the Jewish authorities. But as it is, my kingdom is not of this world!"

Pilate says, "Then you are a king?"

And Jesus replies, "You said it. I am a king. I was born, I came into the world, for this: to testify to the truth. Everyone devoted to the truth listens to my voice."

Pilate, obviously feeling uneasy, gets up, saying, "What is truth?"

And then, turning to the crowd, he says, "I do not find him guilty of any crime."

One of the Pharisees then moves forward and says, "With his teaching he is stirring up unrest all over Judea, from Galilee, where he began, all the way to here."

Pilate says, "You mean he is a Galilean?"

"Yes," says the Pharisee.

Pilate, looking very relieved, says, "Then he belongs to Herod's jurisdiction. Herod is in the city. I will send this man to him."

Pilate orders some of his soldiers to take Jesus to Herod's palace. The crowd, including us, follows at a little distance.

Herod comes out to see what all the noise is about. When he catches sight of Jesus, he says, "Who are you bringing to me?"

The soldiers' officer says, "Pilate has sent this Galilean here for you to deal with. His name is Jesus. He was brought to Pilate by these people."

Herod looks at Jesus and says, "Well, this is my lucky day. For a long time I have been wanting to meet you—I have been hearing so much about you and the amazing things you can do. I have very much been hoping to get to see you perform one of your miracles.

"I guess my chances of that are now pretty good! You do me a big favor, and I do you one, right? Okay, so why are you here?"

Jesus just stands there looking at him, saying nothing.

Clearly unnerved, Herod says, "Fine. If you will not talk to me, I will have to ask the chief priests about you."

And he does that. He asks them, "What seems to be the problem here?"

They repeat to him all that they told Pilate.

Herod spends some time questioning Jesus. But throughout the questioning, Jesus says not one word. And this makes Herod furious.

Finally he looks at the crowd and says, "We have ourselves a silent king." And then he turns to his own guards and says, "Bring one of my old robes and put it on him."

After this has been done, Herod leads his court in mocking and ridiculing Jesus. I once again start to growl and to move toward Jesus. But Mary catches me and picks me up, saying, "No! Jesus would not want you to take a chance on getting hurt. And besides, look how much dignity he is showing as they make fun of him. They think they are making him look ludicrous, but actually his composure is making them look like the fools."

Eventually even Herod realizes this. So he tells Pilate's soldiers, "Take this silent king, in his royal robe, back to Pilate. Jesus is his problem, not mine."

As the soldiers lead Jesus back to Pilate, the Pharisees work on the crowd that is following Jesus. They do whatever it takes to get the people to demand Jesus' death. I hear them bribe some and threaten others.

I can't help it, I am getting furious again. Mary can tell, so she picks me up again and says to me, "Pup, they're jealous of Jesus, and afraid of the good news that he brings. They think that if the people accept his teaching, they will lose the power they have over them. Of course what they are doing is terribly wrong. But we have to remain silent. If we make ourselves known, they will not let us stay and support Jesus."

I know she is right. And, much as I want to do something to the Pharisees, I will follow her wishes.

When we get back to the governor's palace and Pilate comes out again, he looks disgusted. Obviously he thought that this problem was already over with, at least for him.

Mary, meanwhile, has put me down, and now she is so caught up in what is happening that she is not paying attention to me.

I have just got to know what is going on, so I sneak through the crowd and get as close as I can to where Pilate is sitting. The soldiers are so busy watching the crowd for signs of trouble, they ignore me.

Pilate looks at the crowd and says in a loud voice, "You brought this man to me before, and said that he was inciting your people to rebellion. Now, I have already examined him here, in your presence, and I have not found him guilty of any crime. Nor, evidently, has Herod, since he sent him back to me. Certainly this man has done nothing meriting death. I therefore will have him flogged and then let him go."

The crowd shouts, "No! Kill him!"

Pilate just stands there for a few moments, in silence. And then he says, "All right, you know the favor I'm in the habit of doing for you—every year, during the Passover, I set free for you one prisoner, of your choosing. Well, which of these do you want me to release to you: Jesus the King of the Jews, or Barabbas?"

When I hear this, that Pilate is making them choose between Jesus and Barabbas, my heart leaps. I know

Barabbas—he is a thief and a murderer. The people hate him and will not want him back on the streets.

But then I look out at the crowd, and I see the Pharisees moving around in it. They are coaxing and threatening people by saying, "Jesus has been found guilty by our high priest and chief priests; is that not evidence enough?"

While Pilate is waiting for the people to make their choice, a servant comes up to him and says, "I have a message from your wife."

I move even closer, so that I can hear what Pilate is told.

The servant says, "Her message is, 'Have nothing to do with that righteous man. I had a dream about him today which caused me terrible suffering.'"

Pilate now looks very concerned. So my hope for Jesus grows stronger.

But a moment later, my heart sinks. I hear the people shout, "Give us Barabbas!" I run back to Mary.

When I turn around, I see Pilate shake his head and just stand there for a few moments.

Then he walks back to Jesus, and says to him, "Maybe there is another way. I don't find you guilty of anything, but they want blood, so we will give them some blood and see if that satisfies them."

He turns and gives orders to one of his officers, and Jesus is taken away.

Everyone waits to see what will happen next. Mary looks horrified.

All of a sudden we hear the crack of a lash, and then the moan of someone in pain. After the second crack, I recognize the cry. My Master is being whipped.

I will *not* let this happen. I make a bolt for the palace.

But John catches me. Holding me fast, he says, "Pup, you can't help him now. And if he sees you hurt, it will only make it harder for him. You must stay here with us."

I know he is right, but I am so angry, I am shaking.

The whipping seems to go on forever.

Then there is deathly quiet. It is like that for a few minutes. But then we hear one more loud groan of pain.

A few minutes later, Pilate again comes out to the people and asks, "Who do you want me to release to you?" He motions with one hand, and the guards bring out Barabbas. Barabbas has nothing but contempt on his face, and the people shout curses at him. Pilate says, "Do you want Barabbas? Or do you want the King of the Jews?" He motions with the other hand, and the guards drag out Jesus.

His body is covered with blood, from the whipping. And they have put on his head a mock crown, made out of thorns, which makes blood run down his face. And that robe that Herod dressed him in, they have put back on him, to make him look like a mock king.

The crowd is all worked up, and again keeps shouting, "Give us Barabbas!"

Pilate shakes his head, and then says to Jesus, "What can I do? You will not speak to me. And why won't you? Don't you realize that I have the power to set you free, or to have you crucified?"

Jesus says, "You would not have any power over me had it not been given you from above. And therefore the one who handed me over to you has the greater guilt."

Pilate comes back to the people and shouts, "I do not find Jesus guilty of anything! I see no reason not to set him free!"

One of the Pharisees steps up and shouts, "If you set him free, you are no friend of the emperor! Anyone who claims to be a king is a rebel against the emperor!"

Pilate sits on the seat of judgment and says, "Bring me some water."

Water is brought. Pilate washes his hands, making sure everyone sees him do this, and shouts, "I am innocent of this man's blood! See to it yourselves!"

The priests and elders and all the people they have stirred up shout back, "Let it be on us and on our children!"

Pilate releases Barabbas, and then, in a shaky voice, he gives Jesus his sentence. He says, "Jesus, King of the Jews, you are to be crucified. It will be done this very day."

Then he turns to his guards and says, "Take him away and make the necessary preparations, and do the deed quickly."

Mary bursts into tears. John lets go of me and puts his arm around her—and it does seem to help. Her face is still racked with pain, but she seems to understand more about what is happening than the rest of us do.

I don't know what to do. I am frantic with worry. How can this come to any good? I know Jesus told me to trust him that everything will work out. But crucifixion is so final. How will I ever survive without my Master?

25

"They Do Not Know What They Are Doing"

John is so concerned with taking care of Mary, he is not paying attention to me.

I can no longer stand around doing nothing. I *have* to go to Jesus.

I run through the crowd and go to the palace gate. All the guards are busy keeping control of the crowd, so I am able to slip in. I go looking for the place where they are keeping Jesus.

I find a wall with barred windows. This must be the jail; so Jesus is probably here.

I walk along the wall, sniffing as carefully as I can. I hope to find Jesus' distinctive scent.

At the third window I pick up a strong smell of blood— and mixed in with it, his scent. I stand by the window, whimpering and crying. I hear a groan of pain, and then the sound of someone moving. I hold my breath and think, Please let it be Jesus.

Then I see Jesus' face at the window. It is streaked with blood, and there is pain in his eyes. But when he sees me, he smiles.

He says, "Hi, Pup! I'm so glad to see you. You bring me such joy. And I know you wouldn't be here if Mom wasn't being taken care of."

I jump up, trying to get closer to the window, but I can't.

It hurts me that I can't get closer and give some comfort to my Master. But he sees how upset I am, and whispers, "It's okay. You don't need to be any closer. It's nice that you're there. And my Father is with me at all times. He is my comfort and strength no matter what I have to endure. And by completing my mission from him, I will be everyone's redemption. You may not understand now what I am saying, but you will. Remember what I told you—everything will be fine, because everything is in God's providence.

"But when they bring me out of the cell, be careful not to get in the way. I don't want you hurt in any way. And don't forget, everything will work out, no matter what they do to me. Even death is not the end. Your heart will break, but you have to trust me and believe what I say. I wish that all of you that I love so much would not have to go through the suffering of watching me die. But the glory of the good news can only be completed through and after my death."

When I hear all this, I am both devastated and excited; filled with sadness, but also hope.

Just then, I hear the door of the cell being opened. Jesus looks at me and says with a sigh, "Pup, it is time for me to fulfill the last request given me by my Father. Good-bye for now."

I run around to the other side of the jail, and get there just as they are bringing Jesus out. I notice that his hands are tied with a rope.

By now the crowd waiting to see him is huge. Many of those spies who were always following us are here, and so are many of the people from the trial. The spies and these others all keep sneering at Jesus and shouting, "Crucify him!"

And there are those who have come from the town just out of curiosity. But also I see many of the people that Jesus helped in the past. They are saying nothing, and are looking sad and confused at what is happening, like they can't believe that Jesus is going to be killed.

Two other men are taken out of the jail and put with Jesus. Their hands are also tied, but I can see that these two prisoners have not been whipped.

All three are untied. Jesus still has on the red robe that Pilate had them put back on him after the flogging—the ratty old robe that Herod threw onto him. I can see dried blood on it. The soldiers rip it off his back, and Jesus winces in pain and starts bleeding again. I start to move forward, but Jesus looks at me and shakes his head no. This makes me remember the warning he gave me, "Be careful not to get in the way."

Even though watching this is breaking my heart, I will obey my Master.

One of those Pharisee spies sees me and says to the soldiers' officer, "That's his dog. Kill it."

The officer replies, "I have no such orders."

The Pharisee shouts back, "Then chase it away!"

The officer says sharply, "You have no authority over me. I will do my job as I see fit. As long as the dog doesn't cause me any problems, I will let it be."

The soldiers make the three prisoners each take a heavy plank on their shoulders, and they tie their hands to the ends of the plank. The one they make Jesus carry is the biggest and heaviest.

Then one of the soldiers points at a hill and says, "See, at the top there, where those three uprights are standing? That is called Skull Place, and it is where the three of you will die. Now get moving; we don't want this to take all day."

As the prisoners move forward, some of the people make rude remarks. Others just watch in disbelief. I walk alongside Jesus, trying to be close, but also to not get in the way, as Jesus instructed me. All of my attention is on him. I'm not really paying any attention to the crowd; I'm only focusing on my Master.

He is so weak, he stumbles and falls—and the plank hits his head. He lies there, exhausted. I wonder if he will ever be able to get up. But I do not move closer to him; I must keep out of the way.

One of the soldiers takes his staff and pokes Jesus in the side. It makes me think of all the times I felt that same pain, when I was a stray.

Jesus starts to get up, but then he stops, and stares into the crowd. I look in that direction, and there I see Mary and John and the women who helped Mary with the Passover meal.

The other women are crying, but Mary is fighting back her tears. I think she doesn't want to cause Jesus more pain by letting him see how much all this is hurting her.

John again has his arm around her. Jesus looks at the two of them, and nods and smiles as if to tell them, as he did me, "Everything will be all right."

The soldier pokes Jesus again and shouts, "Get up! No stopping to rest! Keep moving!" So Jesus gets up and slowly and painfully moves on, leaving his mother behind.

It's the hottest time of day, and Jesus is sweating a lot. The dust and dirt from his fall are now caked with his blood. And the path is getting steeper, and Jesus is having a harder time walking with that plank tied to him.

Now the sky is getting darker, and I hear thunder in the distance.

Jesus is passing by a group of women who are crying very loudly. I don't recognize them, but from the way that they're dressed, I think they are probably wives and daughters of the elders, Pharisees, and teachers. Jesus says to them, "Daughters of Jerusalem, do not cry for me; cry instead for yourselves and for your children. For indeed, the days are coming when people will say, 'How lucky are the women who never had children, who never gave birth to babies or nursed them!' In those days people will say to the mountains, 'Fall on us!' and to the hills, 'Hide us!' For if such things as these are done when the wood is green, what will happen when it is dry?"

A little later, Jesus stumbles again, and this time he falls on both knees, gashing them open to the bone. Once again he just lies there; and this time, no matter how often the soldier pokes him, he does not move.

The officer comes up and says, "What's wrong? Why have we stopped?"

The soldier answers, "This Jesus has been flogged too much. If he doesn't get some help with the plank, I'm afraid he will die before we get to the top of the hill."

The officer says sharply, "We can't let that happen."

The officer then calls over a man who looks strong, and asks him, "What is your name?"

The man says, "Simon."

The officer asks him, "Are you one of this man's followers?"

Simon replies, "I'm from Cyrene; I'm just passing through. I've never seen this man. I just saw the crowd and was curious as to what is going on."

"Well," the officer says, "we'll give you an up-close look at that. Help him get up from the ground. Then you will help him carry the plank for a while."

Simon protests, "I've done nothing wrong. Why should I help him?"

The officer, putting his hand on his sword, says, "Because I say so."

Simon angrily helps Jesus up and then hoists the plank onto his own shoulders.

Jesus looks into Simon's eyes and says, "Thank you for your help. I will not forget you."

Instantly a change comes over Simon. He is no longer angry. In fact, he looks happy to be helping this man whom he just met. He looks down at me, and I bark my own thanks.

Jesus tells him, "That's my dog."

After Simon has been carrying the plank for a while, the officer comes over to him and says, "That is enough rest for him. You may go now. Let him finish this, his last walk, on his own."

Simon replies, "I can take the plank the rest of the way for him. It's no problem."

The officer, again putting his hand on his sword, says, "I told you to leave. You don't want to make me tell you again. Unless, that is, you would like a taste of my steel?"

Simon looks at Jesus and says to him, "I have a family. I had better not get into trouble. I'm sorry. But I am glad to have walked this much of the way with you. What is your name?"

Jesus smiles and answers, "I am Jesus. And thank you again for your kindness."

Simon, as he is leaving, calls out, "I will never forget you, Jesus!"

We are now near the top of the hill. Jesus is getting weaker with every step.

Just when we reach the top of the hill, he collapses. They decide to leave him where he is and hang up the other two men first.

They are not paying attention to me, so I sneak up to Jesus and lick his face. He opens his eyes and whispers, "Thank you, Pup, for staying with me. The worst is yet to come."

I think to myself, How can they do any more to my Master? And I lick him again, trying to let him know that no matter what happens, I will not leave him.

Jesus says, "Good, Pup. But now, better back off; they're about to come for me."

I do as he says, and it's just in the nick of time. A few seconds longer and I would have been caught.

I look around and see that many people have come to witness Jesus' final moments of life. But it is quiet now. Even our enemies seem shaken by what Jesus has had to endure. I also see that Mary and John are here, and that Mary Magdalene and another lady named Mary have joined them. This other Mary is some kind of relative.

The soldiers come back and pick Jesus up. They untie his hands from the plank and take it from him, and lay it on the ground. Then, in front of the whole crowd, they strip him, tossing his clothing off to the side. Many in the crowd are smirking and making crude comments. They seem to enjoy his humiliation. I want *so* bad to run up and bite them. But I must obey my Master.

Finally the officer comes over and says to the soldiers, "What are you doing?"

One of them answers, "Having some fun with this fool."

The officer says angrily, "Pilate told us to do the deed quickly. He did not tell us to mock him; he only said to crucify him. Now get it done!"

The officer then walks away, because there is a problem in the crowd. I am happy that he came over to end Jesus' humiliation. I also feel that he has respect for Jesus and would prefer not to be in charge of this assignment.

I look at where the uprights are, and I see that the other two prisoners are already hanging there, each of them having been fastened to his upright and plank.

Jesus is now laid on top of his plank, and long nails are driven into his wrists. He groans in pain. I am just beside myself. To not be allowed to do anything makes *me* almost die of pain.

Then they tie a rope to the plank and slowly raise it up. As Jesus' feet leave the ground, his body's weight pulls on the nails, tearing against the flesh and bones of his wrists, but the nails do hold him fast.

The soldiers lift him up, higher and higher, and then nail his feet to the upright. He gives out a cry that again makes me almost die of pain.

When the shock of it is over, he calls out in a strong voice, "Forgive them, Father! They do not know what they are doing."

The soldiers gather up his clothing, and divide it among themselves. But there is this one fine robe that he wore—it has no seams. It was made by Mary. They roll dice for this prize.

With them out of my way, I go lie down right by Jesus' cross.

One of the soldiers lunges at me, saying, "Get away from there, you mutt!" But the officer growls at him, "You will leave that man's dog alone. It can stay there as long as it likes. This dog is only being loyal to its master. You, as soldiers, should be able to respect that quality."

He then gives me a salute! I sit up, hoping that he knows I am thanking him. And he does; he smiles and nods to let me know.

After Jesus has been on the cross for some time, one of the Pharisees walks up and sneers at him, "Well, well, well, just look at you now, you who were going to tear down the Temple and build it back up in three days! If you are God's Son, save yourself! Come down from that cross!"

I growl at him, and he hurries away.

Then one of the chief priests stands in front of the cross and says snickeringly, "He saved others? He can't even save himself. So this is the king of Israel! Let him come down off that cross right now—then we will believe in him! He trusted in God and claimed to be God's Son—all right, then, let's see if God wants to save him!"

I growl him away too.

But Jesus just looks at every one of these people in a forgiving way. I can't believe how much love my Master has.

Later, one of the elders stands in front of the cross and looks up at Jesus. At first he doesn't say anything, so I don't pay much attention to him. But then I hear him mutter, "What's this?"

He goes over to our friend the officer, and says demandingly, "Take down that sign that is over his head."

"Why?" asks the officer.

"Because," the elder explains, "it says 'Jesus, King of the Jews.' What it should say is 'This man *said*, "I am the King of the Jews." ' "

The officer smiles and says, "Pilate was wondering if anyone would notice. He knew you were all against this man only because of jealousy. He instructed me to tell anyone who raised any objection, 'What I have written, I have written.' You can't do a thing about it. It stays as it is."

I now begin to realize just how much Pilate would have liked to help Jesus. And I am starting to see God's hand in everything that is happening. I have to keep believing what Jesus told me—"Everything will work out." But standing here, right by his cross, I have a hard time believing that I will ever again be happy.

It seems like he has been hanging on that cross for an awfully long time. By now the sky has gotten very threatening, and, other than the soldiers, the only people still here by his cross are John and three women, including Jesus' mother.

Now one of the criminals crucified along with him starts insulting him, saying, "Hey, aren't you the Messiah? Save yourself, and us too while you're at it!" But the other one says to that one, "Have you no fear of God? We got the same sentence as this man. It was only right that we got it; we deserve it, for our crimes. But he's done nothing wrong." And then, looking at Jesus, he says, "Remember me, Jesus, when you come into your kingdom."

Jesus turns to him and says, "I promise you, today you will be with me in paradise."

It is now the middle of the afternoon, although it's hard to tell because the sky is black as night. Mary and the other women and John come up close; they stand next to me. We all look up, and Jesus raises his head to see us better.

Then, with great effort, he says to Mary, "Woman, look, your son!"

Then he says to John, "Look, your mother!"

And then he looks at me, and I feel as though he's saying, "Pup, as you have been to me, be to them."

A little later he says, in a loud and heartbreaking voice, "My God! My God! Why have you abandoned me?"

And then, not as loudly, he says, "I'm thirsty."

One of the soldiers gets a sponge and soaks it in sour wine. Another one says, "Wait—let's see if God comes to save him!" But the one with the sponge says, "Have you no pity? Look at how he is suffering. This will help him."

Jesus takes a sip, and then, in a firm voice, he says, "Father, I put my spirit into your hands."

I sense the life going out of Jesus, and I let out one loud and very long howl of grief. Over my howl we hear him shout, "It is finished!" And then he dies.

At that moment there is a blinding flash of lightning and a deafening clap of thunder. The ground shakes; I think this could be an earthquake. Mary is crying quietly, and John is holding her, and also crying. I hear our officer friend exclaim, "He really was the Son of God!"

It is starting to get late, and it is very dark. The soldiers want to finish their job and go home. So they start breaking the legs of the prisoners, to get them to die sooner. But when they are done with the other two and are about to start on Jesus, they see that he is already dead, so they do not break his legs.

Then three men suddenly show up, and one of them says to the officer, "Pilate sent me to tell you that he wants you to turn the body over to these two men. And he said to make sure Jesus is dead. Also, he told me to inform you that the Pharisees are afraid that Jesus' disciples will steal his body away, and so they are going to send a contingent of the Temple Guard to watch over the tomb that his body is put in. When the Temple Guard arrives, your duty is completed."

I recognize these other two men. Their names are Joseph and Nicodemus. Joseph is from Arimathea and is a member of the Sanhedrin, the Jews' supreme council. He is a follower of Jesus, but up to now he has kept this a secret, for fear of the Pharisees.

As soon as the messenger has left, the officer takes a spear from one of the guards. He whispers, "Jesus, I now know that you are the Son of God. Please do not take offense at what I am about to do. I am under orders. And your body is dead, so this will not cause you any pain." Then he sticks the spear in Jesus' right side. Jesus does not move. But, instantly, blood and water flow out from his side.

Joseph and Nicodemus take him down, and lay him in Mary's arms. Mary cries, and cradles Jesus' head, and keeps stroking and kissing it.

I lick his hand, and there is no life in it. I smell no life in his body; all I smell is death. But I remember that he told me to have trust in his words. I will not let my Master down.

Joseph and Nicodemus very gently take Jesus' body from Mary, and they wrap it in linen sheets and a headcloth, along with spices; that's how Jews prepare a body for burial. Then these two men gently carry the body to a tomb in a garden.

Our officer friend has the soldiers march behind the body, as if they were an honor guard. I think to myself, The Pharisees would sure not like this.

I sniff the place that Jesus is being put into, and I notice that there is no smell of death. It is a new tomb.

After they place him in it, the soldiers roll a gigantic stone in front of it; and I lie down in front of the stone.

Mary looks at me and says gently, "Pup, come home with me. There is nothing more you can do."

I love Mary, but I am not about to leave my Master. I don't know what he meant when he told me that everything will work out, but I have to be here when it happens.

Mary says softly, "Please, Pup, it is useless for you to stay here."

I put my head down and refuse to leave.

Finally the officer comes over to Mary and says, "I know how much that dog loves Jesus. You are wasting your time. A dog as faithful as this one will never leave its master, even in death. I will make sure nothing happens to it. What's its name?"

Mary says, "PupPup—that's the name Jesus came up with when he took the dog home with him from an alley. And I'm sure you're right. Pup is not about to leave Jesus. We'll be back later to see to the tomb; maybe then Pup will come home with us. But in the meantime, thank you for your offer of protection."

John leads Mary and the other women away.

The officer looks at me and says, "PupPup, your faithfulness is something that I seldom see. But as a soldier I can tell you that if you want to guard the tomb of your master, it would be wise for you to be less visible. When those men from the Temple Guard come, I don't think they will take too kindly to your being here."

I realize that he's right, so I get up and move to a place I can keep watch from without being seen. It's a little opening on a hillside.

The officer looks up at me and says, "Well done, Pup. Yes, that's a good place. A small cave covered by bushes— they won't see you hiding in there."

Then we hear men marching in our direction. The officer quickly says to me, "Stay still, and be careful. I will be leaving now. The Temple Guard is coming."

When the Temple guards arrive, our officer friend tells their leader, "Everything is secure. It is now up to you to keep it that way." And the Roman soldiers leave.

I stay hidden, feeling sad and puzzled. I wonder how Jesus' words can come true. I mean his words, "You will have a joy beyond anything you can imagine."

What did he mean?

Even though I'm alone, I still feel the presence of my Master.

26

"You Will Have a Joy"

I stay hidden all of Friday night. None of the Temple guards has seen me. It is still raining. I am nice and dry in my little cave, while they are getting very wet.

In a way I feel sorry for them. The ones I wish were out in this storm are the chief priests and the Pharisees—the ones responsible for my Master being in the tomb.

Even though I am still alone, I don't feel lonely. I could swear, I feel the presence of my Master.

The only thing I feel bad about is not being with Mary. I hope she's not upset with me for not obeying her and going home with her. But she is Jesus' mother, and I'm sure she understands that I just had to stay with my Master.

Now the sun is coming up. I didn't get much sleep; I couldn't stop thinking about all that I've experienced since Jesus found me. Right now I think about all the times he and I prayed together watching the sunrise.

Even though he is not with me like he used to be, I feel at peace. I am surprised that I feel the way I do. I miss him, but at the same time I really do believe what he told me: "You will have a joy beyond anything you can imagine."

I look down from my hiding place, and I see that the Temple guards are not at peace. They are wet and tired and in a bad mood. One of them irritably grumbles, "What fools the Pharisees are, having us guard a dead man. What do they think he's going to do, come back to life?" And then another one warns him, "You better watch your mouth. If they hear you talking like that, you may be joining him in the tomb!"

I drift off to sleep. I guess all the events of yesterday, and my almost sleepless night, have finally caught up with me.

At about noon, I am awakened by a familiar voice. I look out of my little cave and see my friend the Roman officer. The leader of the Temple Guard also recognizes him, but is not happy to see him. He says, "What are you doing here? You think we can't even take care of guarding a dead man?"

"That's not it at all," says the officer. "Today is my day off. And after the day I had yesterday, I can really use it. When I was here yesterday, I noticed some unusual rock formations up on that hill. So I thought this would be as good a day as any to check them out."

One of the Temple guards says sarcastically, "Yeah, right. A Roman officer is interested in rocks."

The officer replies, "You never know when you'll find a precious stone."

Another guard laughs and says, "Now that does sound like a Roman officer. Who ever heard of one who wasn't always looking for a way to add to his purse?"

As the officer starts walking up the hill, he asks the guards, "Did you have any problems last night?"

Their leader answers, "None at all, except for the constant rain. Other than that, it was quiet as the grave." He laughs, and then says, "We saw nothing all night."

When my friend gets to where I'm hiding, he sits down next to me. And then I realize just how good a place this is, because he too is hidden from the Temple Guard.

He looks at me and says, "Pup, it seems you have kept your presence a secret from the Temple guards. I thought you might be getting hungry and thirsty."

He takes out a bowl and fills it with water from his water bottle, and then he puts some meat in front of me. When I smell it, I realize how hungry I am.

I eat and drink all that he gives me, and when I'm done I lick his hand to show him my appreciation.

He pets me, and says, "Pup, I have been hearing about your master. Many people have been saying that he claimed to be the Son of God, and any of his followers I have talked to believe that he was all that he claimed to be. And I felt it myself when I saw him die."

He pauses, and then says, "Well, now some are even saying that he promised to rise from the dead."

He pauses again, and then, looking into my eyes as if trying to read my mind, he asks, "Is that why you were so insistent on staying here last night?"

I lick him in the face, and this startles him. He says, "Is that a yes?"

I wag my tail.

I hope he will search out some of Jesus' disciples and learn all about the good news. I would love for him to be one of Jesus' followers.

He whispers, "I'd better go. We don't want them to

think that I've found some real valuable rock, and follow me up here, and find you. Take care of yourself, Pup. I will leave this bowl here with some water and a little more food. Your master was truly lucky to have such a loyal friend. I hope to see you again."

As he leaves, I think to myself, No, I am the lucky one, to have such a loving master as Jesus.

The rest of the day, nothing much happens. The guards continue to grumble about their duty being useless.

When night comes, I slip off to sleep again, feeling almost as if I'm sleeping on Jesus' lap.

▲▼▲▼▲

I wake up early. The sky is just starting to turn rosy. Some of the Temple guards are asleep, while others are standing around talking.

Just when the sun breaks over the horizon, there is a sudden noise. It sounds like an earthquake. But nothing is moving. The guards all jump to their feet and draw their swords.

All of a sudden the gigantic stone that is blocking the entrance to Jesus' tomb starts to move. I am the first to see it, but then the guards do too. They start to move away, but their leader orders them to stay close to the tomb.

I am so excited I can't keep myself hidden. I run down closer to the tomb—but still being careful not to get too close to the Temple guards. Then, as if it weighed nothing, that huge stone rolls completely away from the tomb. And then there comes from within the tomb a light so bright that it makes the sun look dull.

An angel comes out of the tomb. It's the angel that came to Jesus in Gethsemane, before his arrest. Only this time the angel's clothing is as white as snow, and the angel's face is like lightning.

The Temple guards have their swords drawn, but are frozen with terror.

In a loud voice the angel says, "If you choose to use your swords, know that you will die where you stand. If you would live, put your swords away and leave in peace."

The guards look at one another and quickly decide not to fight. They hurriedly leave the garden.

The angel looks at me, and in a quieter voice says, "Pup, your Master—Jesus, the Son of the living God—has done what he said he would do. He has conquered death.

"In a short time you will see him. But he asks that you hide out for a little while longer. Mary Magdalene, Joanna, Salome, Mary the mother of James, and some of the other women followers of Jesus will soon be arriving with spices they have prepared for the body. Jesus does not want them to be frightened, so he is going to break his resurrection to them slowly. You will have a part in this. When you see your Master, come and stand next to him. Until then, go back to your hiding place."

I am so happy, I want to see Jesus right now! But I understand his concern for the women, and of *course* I would obey him anyway. So I go back to my little cave.

When I am settled in it, I notice that the Temple guards have gotten back together, on this very hill. From my position I can both see them and hear what they are saying.

I see that one of the leaders of the Pharisees is with them now. He says to them, "Why are you all here? You're supposed to be guarding the tomb. What's the matter with you? Why are you all shaking?"

The leader of the Temple Guard tells him what has happened.

The Pharisee, now sounding pretty shaken himself, says, "That is all we need. There will be no stopping Jesus' followers now."

For a while he just stands there, looking worried, obviously trying to figure out what to do. And then a sly look comes over his face.

He says to the Temple guards, "Here's what we do. You tell everyone that you fell asleep, and that while you were asleep, Jesus' followers came and stole the body away."

The leader replies, "If we tell them that, we'll be punished for neglect of duty."

"No," says the Pharisee, "the whole council will cover for you. You will not get in trouble. And we will make sure you are well paid for this."

Then they all take off together, heading back to the city.

I think to myself, How can he make up lies like that about what Jesus has done? He must be under the influence of the Evil One.

But as I wait for the women to arrive, I notice the sunrise again. It is the most beautiful one I've ever seen. It is all tinged with hope, because all that my Master told me has come true. I already have a joy beyond anything I could have imagined.

27

"Your Joy Will Remain"

From my hiding place I see some of the women come into the garden. They are crying.

I want to comfort them. I want to let them know that their sadness is about to turn into joy. I am so excited that I can hardly keep from running up to them. But I will do as my Master has asked.

Mary Magdalene stops at the garden gate. She is very distressed. She sits down, obviously finding it difficult to bring herself to the tomb.

The other women comfort her and talk her into coming with them to the tomb.

I see their surprise at finding the stone rolled away, and then I see amazement.

As they are staring at the tomb, the angel steps out and stands at the entrance. Now they are terrified, but the angel, in a gentle voice, says to them, "You must not be afraid. I know you are looking for Jesus, who was crucified. He is not here; he did rise, just as he said he would. Come see the place where he lay. And then go quickly and tell his disciples, 'He is risen from the dead, and is going ahead of you to Galilee. He will meet you there.'"

The women go up to the entrance and look in, and their faces shine with joy. And immediately all of them except Mary Magdalene run off to tell the disciples. She says to the others, "You go on and start telling them. I want to stay here for a while. I need to think about what we've been told."

I sense that she needs some comforting, so I decide to go to her. But just as I'm about to leave my hiding place, I see John run past me, and without thinking, I run after him.

He stops at the entrance of the tomb. He just bends down and looks in, from there. I also look in for the first time.

There's a kind of glow coming from inside, but it seems to be coming from nowhere in particular.

While John and I are looking in, Peter arrives, out of breath from running. He looks at me and asks, "Where did you come from, Pup? And where is Jesus' body?"

I bark at the sky. But Peter doesn't get what I'm trying to tell him.

He goes into the tomb. And John and I follow him.

In the tomb we see the linen sheets, and the cloth that had been around Jesus' head. It's not with the sheets; it's rolled up in a place by itself. The glowing light that I saw from outside seems to be coming from the walls themselves. And I notice that the smell of the place is entirely different from what it was before they put Jesus' body in it. The tomb now has the sweet smell of the most wonderful spring day. I think to myself, Well, of course; spring is a time of new life, so it is only right that the tomb smells as it does.

Peter leads John and me out of the tomb. He sees Mary Magdalene, and asks her, "When did you get here?"

She says, "I've been here a long time. You ran past me—you just didn't notice me."

Peter says, "I'm sorry. There's just been so much going on, and I don't know how to take it all in. Some of us got together in an out-of-the-way place. We're trying to keep out of sight; there's no telling what the Pharisees will do next; and all of a sudden, we hear banging on the door. We think this is the end of us; that the Temple Guard has found us and we'll be arrested. But when we open the door, we find there, much to our surprise, some of the women disciples. They tell us that the tomb is empty, and that an angel told them, 'Jesus, who was crucified, is not here. He has risen from the dead, and now he is going to Galilee ahead of you, and you will see him there.' I couldn't believe what they were saying. John and I had to come see for ourselves. And now I have to admit, though I don't know what to make of it, that the tomb is empty."

Mary Magdalene says, "Yes! I too have seen the tomb—and the angel! It doesn't seem possible that Jesus did actually rise from the dead, but that is what he said he would do."

Peter says, "John, you go to Jesus' mother and tell her what has happened. I'll gather the others and meet you there."

Then he looks at Mary Magdalene and asks, "Are you coming with us?"

She says, "No. I want to stay here a while—I'm still a little dazed. I'll join you and the others later."

I decide to stay with Mary Magdalene.

Now she stands, glances at the tomb, and starts crying again. I wonder why she is not happy, since she heard what the angel said and has seen that the tomb is empty. I guess she just needs to see Jesus for herself. And I must admit, I too am dying to see my Master.

As I am keeping a protective eye on Mary, I see him walk up behind her! He's looking different, but I have no doubt that it is my Master.

He says, "Ma'am, why are you crying? Who are you looking for?"

She turns to him, but doesn't recognize him. "They have taken my Lord away," she says, "and I don't know where they've put him! If you have taken him away, sir, tell me where you have put him, and I will go and get him."

As she finishes speaking, I come and stand next to Jesus. And then he just says, "Mary!"

She looks at Jesus, and then down at me.

I see the expression on her face change from sadness to confusion, and then joy. She says, "Teacher! It is you!"

Jesus smiles and says, "Yes, it is. All that I told you is true. Now you know how life-giving the good news is! But I can't stay with you right now. I must first go to my Father and your Father. Go join the disciples in Galilee. I'll see you all there."

Then he looks down at me and says, "Hello, Pup! I've missed you!"

I wag my tail and jump up on his leg.

Then he says, "Thank you for staying with me and being my sentry while I was in the tomb. But I'm sorry, Pup, you can't go with me just yet. But I will see you again!"

I feel so sad. I want to go with him *now*.

He still knows my thoughts. He says, "Remember what I told you from the cross? I told you to be with Mom and John the way you have been with me. Your joy will remain, and I will see you later. But now I must leave."

Then Jesus disappears.

Mary Magdalene sits down, and I climb up on her lap. She starts rubbing my ear. She's still crying, but these are tears of joy.

She says, "Pup, I know that was Jesus who was just here, but he looked different. He looked glorious, and yet so warm and loving and approachable that it almost feels like his love just seeped into me."

I have to agree with her. As great and loving as Jesus was before the events of these last three days, he is even greater and more loving now. I didn't think my Master could be greater, but he is.

Mary Magdalene gets up and tells me, "I have to join the others; you run and catch up with John and bring this joy to Mary."

I take off and run as fast as I can.

Before long, I catch up with John, and when I do he looks at me and says, "I can't wait to see Mary and tell her that her son is alive!"

We rush as fast as we can. When we get near the house where Mary is staying, I run ahead, and when I reach the door, I start barking happily and scratch the door.

Mary opens it; I look at her face; and she's smiling! She looks down at me and says, "Well, Pup, have you decided to come home? You should have been here a while ago—my faith in my son has been confirmed."

I guess my confusion shows on my face, because she then says to me, "Do you think that Jesus would not be with both of his parents first?"

I just keep happily barking on and on.

Then John comes to the door and gives Mary a big hug and lifts her off the ground, announcing, "Jesus is alive! He did what he said he would; he rose from the dead!"

Then he says, "It is true. The tomb is empty. Some of the women disciples were met by an angel at the tomb. They were told that Jesus has risen, and that we are all to meet him in Galilee."

Mary holds on to John a long time, crying tears of joy. When she is finally able to speak, she says, "Yes, I already knew. If you and Pup had been here, you would have also seen this greatest of all miracles, my risen son."

Then she lets go of John and hurries us into the house, saying, "Let's not waste time. We have to get everything together for the trip back to Galilee."

When that's all taken care of, we go to where the other apostles are staying. We walk there filled with joy. Mary and John are laughing and recalling so many of the pleasant times they have spent with Jesus. Nothing is said about the last three days. They don't want any gloom to creep into their joy.

As I walk with them, I think of what Jesus told me about this joy I would have that would go beyond anything I could imagine. I must admit that ever since that angel appeared at the tomb, my joy has grown with each new discovery of what the good news really means. It has been worth all the pain of the last three days to experience this latest glory of my Master.

28

"A Ghost Does Not Have Flesh and Bones"

Mary and John and I arrive at the house where the apostles are hiding out. It's the house of the mother of a disciple named Mark.

John knocks on the door, but there's no answer. Finally he calls out, "It's me—John. Mary and Pup are with me. Let us in."

The door slowly opens, and there stands James. As soon as he sees us, he opens the door wide and says, "Hey, did you forget the knock code? We have to be careful, you know."

John says, "We don't need all that now. Jesus is risen and is going to meet us. You know that, don't you?"

We go into a big room. It looks like just about everyone from the Passover meal is here. I run around sniffing and getting petted by everyone. But I notice that someone is missing. I think to myself, I know why Judas isn't here, but where is Thomas?

After a little while, when we're all sitting, John says, "I really don't think we need this security anymore, since Jesus is alive again. He has risen from the dead."

Bartholomew says, "But are we sure that is true? Are we sure it really happened?"

I am starting to get upset with these people. What is wrong with them, to still be doubting? How can they not believe after three whole years of being with Jesus?

John, sounding like he too is a bit annoyed, says, "Peter and I saw the empty tomb. Isn't that right, Peter?"

"Well, yes," says Peter, "it definitely was empty. But I still don't know what to make of that."

James says, "The Temple guards have been telling

everyone, 'We all fell asleep. When we woke up, the body was gone. Jesus' disciples must have stolen his body away and hidden it.' "

John says, "Yeah, right. The entire contingent of the Temple Guard fell asleep at the same time. And so soundly that they would not hear a huge stone being moved. Next thing we'll be hearing is that PupPup had something to do with the disappearance."

When I hear my name, I look up, and see John smiling at me.

"Well," says Peter, "we do need to be careful. Better to be a bit too cautious than to be caught off guard."

Just as he says this, we hear someone knock on the door.

Everyone turns and looks at the door. I get up and run to it—maybe it's my Master!

Then I notice that I'm the only one moving. Everyone else is just staring at the door. I start barking, but all that happens is that some of the disciples try to hush me up.

The knocking gets louder and does not let up, so finally John gets up and opens the door. And when he does, two of Jesus' followers come in, all excited. I only know the name of one of them; it's Cleopas.

He exclaims, "We have seen Jesus!"

Andrew says, "You two sit down and tell us everything."

Cleopas does all the talking. He says, "All right. Well, here we are, on our way back to Emmaus, discussing all the things that have happened over the last few days, and this stranger catches up with us and starts walking with us. He asks us what we're talking about, and comments that we seem a bit upset. I look at him and ask, 'Are you the only visitor to Jerusalem who doesn't know the things that have taken place there in these last few days?'

"The stranger says, 'What things?'

"And we answer, 'About Jesus of Nazareth. He was a very holy man, and the Pharisees had him crucified! We had hoped that he would be the one to set Israel free; we really thought he was the Messiah; but, just day before yesterday, he was killed and buried. And then early this morning, some of the women of our group went to the tomb, and found that the body was not there. They came back saying that an angel appeared to them and told them that Jesus is alive. A couple of the men then went to the tomb, and they found it exactly as the women had said. But him they have not seen.'

"Then this stranger says to us, 'How foolish you are! How slow to believe all the things the prophets wrote! Did not the Messiah have to suffer these things to enter into his glory?' And then he explains to us all the things in Scripture that have to do with Jesus.

"By the time he finishes, we're near Emmaus. The stranger seems to be going on to some other place, but we invite him to stay with us, and he agrees to. And when we sit down to eat, he takes a loaf of bread, blesses it, breaks it, and gives it to us. And then our eyes are opened; we realize that he is Jesus. But at that very moment he disappears.

"This all happened just a little while ago. We left immediately and got over here as fast as we could."

Everyone has been hanging on every word of this story, and now, for a few moments, no one says anything.

Then Philip says, "And before he broke the bread, you had no hint that he was Jesus?"

And Cleopas replies, "Well, yes, there was a hint that we didn't pick up on. When he was speaking with us along the way and explaining the scriptures to us, it did feel like our hearts were burning within us."

Everyone else is too caught up in the story to be aware

of anything else, but I catch a familiar scent. I look around—and there he is! Jesus is standing right there, smiling.

I start to move, but he motions to me to keep still. I can see that he is enjoying the story, and also that he is about to remove any doubt that he has risen.

Finally, in a strong voice, he says to them, "Peace be with you!"

They all turn toward him, and look terrified. Some mumble, "Is it a ghost?"

Jesus says, "Why are you alarmed? Why these doubts in your minds? See by my hands and my feet that it is I myself. Touch me and see for yourselves. A ghost does not have flesh and bones, as you can see that I do."

I can't get through the pack of disciples, so I'm the last to get to Jesus. He sits down at the table, and I jump up on his lap. He starts rubbing my ear, as he always used to do, and he says to them, "Do you have anything to eat?"

And then, looking down at me, he whispers, "Pup, I've really missed you. You never doubted, did you?"

They give him a piece of grilled fish, and he eats it. And while he is eating, he keeps looking around. He's noticed what I noticed earlier. Finally he asks Peter, "Where's Thomas?"

Peter says, "I'm sorry, Lord, I don't know; I couldn't find him. He was devastated when you died. He was afraid that all his doubts might turn out to be justified. I think he's just really depressed and wanting to be alone for a while. I'm sure he'll come back soon. And then won't he be surprised!"

Jesus says, "But Peter, it's not only Thomas who had a hard time believing that I would rise. Even when you saw the empty tomb, you still didn't believe." Peter nods, and looks ashamed.

Then Jesus says, "And all of you, weren't you still doubting even though I sent the women to you to tell you of my resurrection?" And motioning to Cleopas and his friend, he says, "And then after hearing the whole story of these last two that I sent you, you were still in doubt. If you're going to be my followers and continue to spread the good news, you're going to have to believe with all your heart."

They are all looking sheepish and staying very quiet. I think that each of them is searching his own heart.

Then Jesus says, "As the Father has sent me, I also send you."

And then he breathes on them, and says, "Receive the Holy Spirit. If you forgive anyone's sins, they are forgiven; if you retain anyone's sins, they are retained."

Then Jesus calls me over and whispers to me, "Pup, I need to let them think for a while about what I have just said and done. So I'll be leaving. But don't worry, I'll be back. You have been faithful to me through it all. I hope the disciples will use you as an example of how strongly my followers must believe in me and in the good news which I have brought." After saying this, Jesus fades away.

It is a while before the others notice that Jesus has disappeared. They are all so occupied with reflecting on things—but that is what Jesus wants them to be doing.

No one leaves, but everything stays very quiet. John, Thaddaeus, James Junior, and some of the others are sitting alone, just thinking. The rest are in small groups, talking about all that has happened in the last few days. I lie down in the corner and watch everyone.

I think to myself, Jesus has certainly got them thinking again. I know that this is good. And though I'm without him again, I know that in some way he is with me and always will be. I have finally realized that once Jesus finds you, and you accept him as your Master, he is with you always.

29

"Peace Be with You!"

The next day, the Roman officer comes over, to see how Mary is doing.

When I come up to greet him, he says, "Pup, I'm surprised to see you here. Have you deserted your post?"

Mary glances at me, looking uncertain as to what she should say. I wag my tail and lick his hand, to let her know that I think she should tell him everything.

Mary says to him, "Have you not heard what has happened?"

"No," he replies, "I was sent on another assignment and have been out of the area. I've just returned, and this is the first place I've come."

Mary says, "Why don't you sit down and have some refreshments, and I'll fill you in on what has happened since you left."

The officer sits down, and I jump up on his lap.

Mary continues, "The reason Pup is not at the tomb is that Jesus is not at the tomb."

The officer says angrily, "What happened to the body? Did the Temple guards desecrate the tomb?"

Mary says, "Oh, no. What happened is that Jesus rose from the dead. Many of us not only have seen the empty tomb, but have actually seen and spoken with him."

The officer, looking flabbergasted, says, "But he was *dead*. Of that I am sure."

Mary says, "Jesus told us that he would rise from the dead. He is more than he seems. Jesus is the Son of God."

The officer replies, "The day after Jesus died, I searched out some of his followers, and they told me that same thing—that he is the Son of God. But I didn't know whether to believe it, even though I had felt it to be true when I saw how he died. I did go to the tomb, though, and I spent some time with Pup."

When he says my name, I look up at him, and he rubs my head.

Then he says, "Pup never left the tomb. I think you knew all along that your Master would return, didn't you, Pup?"

I wag my tail.

And then he says, "I am starting to be attracted by what little I know of Jesus."

Mary says gently, "Why don't you let me have one of his disciples talk to you about what he came to do and to teach?"

The officer nods and says, "That would be good. But for now it will have to be done quietly. It could cause problems."

They get up, and Mary says to him, "I will have Philip come see you. He is very easy to talk to, and none of your friends will suspect a thing."

As he leaves, he gives me another pat on the head and says, "Thank you, Mary. Tell Jesus I'm sorry for the role I played. I was only doing what I thought was my duty. I would like to hear more about his mission. Pup, take care of yourself, and take as good care of Mary as you did of her son."

▲▼▲▼▲

Every day, all of us who were at the Passover meal have been gathering in the room where Jesus last spoke to us. At first, in these gatherings, we just prayed and tried to understand what Jesus' words and actions have taught us, and figure out ways to spread the good news. But then Thaddaeus reminded us that at that last Passover meal Jesus said, "*Do* this as my memorial." After a lot of discussion among them, I could feel the Holy Spirit enlightening the apostles, as Jesus had promised would happen. They came to understand that when they bless bread and wine in the same way that Jesus did at the Passover, the bread becomes, as he said, his body, and the wine his blood. They all came to see that what Jesus did was to give his own self as food, to strengthen his followers in body as well as soul.

From that time on, the apostles and Jesus' other disciples have been sharing this very special meal.

Mary and John always bring me along. I am in some way an important part of the group. I have been treated this way especially ever since Mary told the others about the Roman officer and what he said about me never leaving the tomb.

One day, when the disciples are talking about the good news and how they have to help everyone learn that they have to love one another, Mary says to them, "Before Jesus was born, I was visited by an angel, who told me that I would have as my child the Son of God; that he was coming to bring joy to the world; that, by suffering, he would be everyone's redemption. Now, by this resurrection that we all can attest to, he has conquered death. Because of my son, the Son of the living God, we have nothing to fear."

Mary speaks these words so passionately that the disciples start to understand why the Son of God came to earth.

I am so proud of Mary that I run over and jump on her lap and lick her face, while wagging my tail.

She looks at me and whispers, "PupPup, thank you, but I feel that what I just said came from some higher place. I think that the Helper whom Jesus spoke about had something to do with it."

I believe this is true, but I lick her again, for being open to the Holy Spirit and letting him use her to give the disciples a better understanding of Jesus' message.

Just a week after our first visit from Jesus, we are having another one of our gatherings. Thomas has rejoined the group, but is having problems accepting what everyone is telling him.

The other apostles decide to try again to convince him that Jesus is risen from the dead.

"Jesus was in this very room," Andrew begins.

Peter adds, "I know you might find that hard to believe—I did too—but what Andrew is telling you is true."

Philip says, "He sat and ate with us, and challenged us to quit our doubting."

Thomas has had all he can take. He stands up and says, "Listen, unless and until I see the scars from the nails in his hands, and put my finger into those holes, and put my hand into his side, I am not believing any of this."

He is not even done making this statement when, once again, I catch the scent of my Master!

I think to myself, All right! Thomas is about to get the proof he wants, and then he'll have to swallow that stubbornness and pride.

I notice that most of the others in the room also see Jesus. He is directly behind Thomas.

Jesus, in a strong voice, says, "Peace be with you!"

Thomas turns around, and is startled speechless at finding Jesus right smack in front of him.

Kindly but firmly, Jesus says, "Thomas, put your finger

here in the nail marks, and then reach out your hand and put it in my side. Quit your doubting and believe!"

Thomas falls to his knees and says in a choked-up voice, "My Lord and my God!"

Then Jesus looks at everyone and says, "Do you believe because you see me? More blessed are those who have not seen me and yet believe!"

▲▼▲▼▲

Jesus is now spending a lot of time with us, going over with the disciples everything they will need to remember.

At the end of one of these sessions, the disciples are relaxing. But the lesson is not over—at least not for Peter.

Jesus asks him, "Do you love me more than these others?"

He answers, "Yes, Lord. You know that I love you."

Jesus looks him in the eye and says, "Feed my lambs."

A little later, Jesus says to him, "Do you love me?"

He answers, "Yes, Lord. You *know* I love you."

Jesus says, "Tend my sheep."

Still later, Jesus says to him, "Do you love me?"

Peter, catching on, with the rest of us, why Jesus has asked him this for a third time, looks at first very hurt and then very grateful, and finally says humbly, "Lord, you know everything; you know that I love you."

Jesus then says, "Feed my sheep. You know how, when you were younger, you used to get yourself dressed and go where you wanted? Well, when you are old, you will stretch out your hands and someone else will dress you and take you where you don't want to go."

Peter asks, "Lord, do you mean I will be asked to suffer as you did?"

Jesus nods and says emphatically, "Yes! I am telling you, Follow me."

Then Peter asks, "And what about the others—John, for instance?"

Jesus says, "What concern is that of yours? You are to follow me. That is all you need to know.

"But I will tell you this. You all will have similar roads, but each road will be different. As each of you has different gifts, so each will have a different mission to accomplish in the spreading of the good news. Every one of you has an important part to play in the mission that God started by sending me, his Son."

As the days go by, I can see that the disciples are coming to understand Jesus' teaching more and more, and are becoming more committed to it.

After being with us for a month or so, Jesus tells everyone, "I would like you all to join me near Bethany." And when someone asks why, he just says, "It will soon be clear to you all."

As we are setting out, Jesus tells the disciples, "I would like some private time with Mom and Pup."

Then Jesus and Mary and I walk ahead of the others. They all respect this and make sure to leave a good amount of space between us and them.

Jesus first speaks to Mary. He says, "Mom, it is time for me to go to my real home. My Father is calling me back to heaven. I know you will miss me, but I will not be gone as I was before. I will always be watching over you. And you will join me; I will have a special place for you. But for now I need you to stay here. When I was dying I told you that you were to be the mother of John; now I need you to be mother not only to John and the other apostles, but to all my followers. I am your son, but they too are your children. I have told them that God is my Father, and that they can also call God their Father, and they will be calling you Mother. Also, I need you to look after Pup."

Mary gives him a hug and says, "From the moment the angel came to me before you were born, I knew that you would have to go back to heaven. But I will miss you, and always hold you close in my heart. And as for your shadow"—she glances at me—"I remember when you brought the precious pooch home, and so brought even more love into our home. When you left and asked Pup, 'Will you stay with Mary or follow me?' I was the one who told our little friend, 'Go with Jesus; I know where you belong.' I suppose it's now time to tell Pup to stay with me. PupPup will be another little reminder of you. And I am proud to be the Mother of all your followers."

When I hear Jesus say that Mary will be taking care of me, I have mixed feelings. I do love her, so much, but I still want to be with Jesus.

Once again, Jesus knows what I'm thinking. He looks down and says to me, "Pup, I need you to stay here. You can help take care of Mom as you did me. You were always there when I needed someone to talk to or be a friend; Mom will need the same love and support. And you can help keep my apostles on the right track. Like Mom and the other women and John, you stayed by me through everything. Like them, you did not doubt anything I said. Your presence will remind the apostles of what it means to be loyal."

I am sad that I will not get to go with my Master, but I am also proud to be given such an important task. I bark and wag my tail, to say to Jesus that I accept the challenge to stay and help with the work of spreading the good news.

We stop at a hill just outside Bethany, and wait for the rest to gather around. When everyone is here, Jesus says in a voice that thrills us all, "The Holy Spirit will come upon you, and you will be filled with power, and you will be witnesses for me in Jerusalem, all through Judea and

Samaria, and to the ends of the earth! Go, then, to all peoples everywhere and make them my disciples: baptize them in the name of the Father, and of the Son, and of the Holy Spirit, and teach them to carry out all that I have commanded you. And look, I am with you always, to the end of the world."

As he is speaking, Jesus starts rising right up into the heavens. He blesses us all, and then disappears.

We are standing there, trying to still see him, when two angels dressed all in shining white appear beside us. One of them says, "Why are you standing here looking at the sky? Jesus is with his Father and yours, and he is also with you, at the same time. Go back, and wait for the Spirit that he promised to send you. The Holy Spirit will open your minds to all that Jesus taught you." And then the angels disappear.

We look at one another, and stay quiet a long time.

Finally Peter says, "Everyone go back to Jerusalem, to the upstairs room in the house of Mary, Mark's mother. We will make that our base. There we will be united in prayer, with Mary, Jesus' mother, who is now also our mother, and with all of Jesus' followers. We will await the coming of the Holy Spirit whom Jesus has promised us."

We all head off together, filled with joy. Now we are one big family—God's family.

As I walk with Mary, I think about my life, how blessed I am for having had Jesus find me and bring me home. And how blessed I still am to have, no matter where I am, Jesus always with me as my Master.